# The Undersea Adventure

# Philippe Diolé

# THE UNDERSEA ADVENTURE

Translated by Alan Ross

Readers Union

Sidgwick and Jackson

LONDON 1954

THIS Readers Union edition was produced in 1954 for sale to its members only by Readers Union Ltd at 38 William IV Street, Charing Cross, London, and at Letchworth Garden City, Hertfordshire. Full details of RU may be obtained from either of these addresses. This edition has been newly set in 11 point Bembo type, one point leaded, printed and bound by The Ferndale Book Company Ltd at London and Worcester. The book was first published by Albin Michel, Paris, under the title 'L'Aventure Sous-Marine', in 1951; this translation was published by Sidgwick and Jackson Ltd in 1953.

# Preface

ABOOK owes more to its readers than to its author. The author's work ends on the last page of his book, but only its readers give it life. Nevertheless, a writer can at least express his pleasure when one of his books is translated. I shall not, therefore, hide my satisfaction in knowing that L'Aventure Sous-Marine is going to reach an English public.

I am pleased for many reasons; most of all, perhaps, because the English have such a close and subtle relationship to the sea. But it is primarily a relationship to the sea's surface, in which the wind plays as much part as the water. We, however, are establishing an intimacy with the deep, finding beyond the rough barrier of the waves a motionless and transparent world, a silent kingdom through which we are gradually feeling our way. I am perhaps a little vain about this, but it is not an exclusive and jealous vanity. On the contrary, I wish to welcome as many people as possible, especially my English friends, to this underwater continent. In the Mediterranean we have dreamed of 'humanising' the sea. But it is a dream that cannot be completed without the help of English humanism. We have seen some of the consequences of underwater exploration in the different realms of archæology, psychology and poetry. England will doubtless make a rich contribution to these, and other, spheres in her own way. It is because of this that I welcome the translation of my book.

But we must get off to a good start. So far the exploits of divers have resulted in an impressive and dramatic literature, where fantastic octopuses and fearful sharks swarm to their encounters with men. The reader follows these exotic battles breathless and appalled. This, *however, is no way to attract people below the surface. There is nothing of the kind in* The Undersea Adventure; *rather the opposite. I have tried to make diving an intimate, friendly affair. If there are octopuses, they are playful and harmless companions. I have wanted, if nothing else, to show that life underwater is within the reach of everyone.*

*England, as far as diving is concerned, has nothing to learn from any other country. The inventive genius of Sir Robert Davis and the feats of English frogmen put her in the front rank. But these are show-pieces, due to exceptional scientific gifts and courage. France's contribution has been to familiarise a larger public with the beauty of the deep, to give holiday coasts a new dimension for men and women to explore. The work done by our diving clubs towards this is worth study in England. I don't think she will be long in adopting what is at the same time a sport, an instrument of scientific research and the means towards a new 'human condition'.*

*There will certainly be difficulties especial to northern seas: cold, storms, currents, the excess of seaweeds. I have never dived near the English coast, but the shores of Brittany give one an inkling of what to expect. There will be areas and periods of warmth and calm. The uncertainty of the English climate certainly creates a need for extra care, but it does not, in any sense, make the enjoyment of the underwater world impossible.*

*Let me end by wishing English divers joy in the great pleasures to be had in the discovery of a new world. Perhaps some young poet-diver will, like Theseus, emerge from the sea-depths with a golden ring to shine for us all.*

P. D.

# The Contents

# Acknowledgments to the Illustrations

*Photographs by the Author* – Plates one, two (bottom), three and nine.

*By G. Beuchat-Borelli* – Plates five (A and C), eleven (bottom) and fourteen (bottom).

*By H. Broussard* – Plates two (top), five (D), six (top), seven, eight (bottom), eleven (top), twelve (bottom), thirteen, fourteen (top), fifteen and sixteen.

*By Anita Conti* – Plates five (B) and ten (both subjects).

*By F. Dumas* – Plate twelve (top).

*By Jean Foucher-Créteau* – Plate eight (top).

# The Illustrations

*The plates appear as a group between pages 28 and 29*

I T is only fair that I write, at the outset of this book, the name of my friend Capitaine de Corvette Philippe Tailliez, who first opened my eyes to the underwater world. Georges Bertrand was not only the ideal companion in many dives but was always at hand with help and encouragement. Professor Drach and Professor Pérès have been more than ready to put their knowledge and their work at my disposal. M. Fernand Benoit, Director of the XIIth Archaeological Survey Department, has been good enough to discuss with me the possibilities of underwater excavation.

Finally, I must thank my friends Anita Conti, Henri Broussard, Georges Beauchat and Jean Foucher-Créteau, who gave me permission to reproduce some of their photographs as illustrations to this book.

# I

# First Beginnings

*I can only think of one experience that might exceed in interest a few hours spent under water and that would be a journey to Mars.*
WILLIAM BEEBE

I HAVE no 'stories' to tell.

Breaking the surface of the sea, roaming about in the deep waters of the ocean, going down slowly, eyes open, watching the flicker of mullet and the dance of sea-bream, the butterflies of these liquid skies: this does not make up a 'story'.

But if I do not know any stories, I have perhaps lived a miracle, one which I want to talk about: I have travelled to another world in which 'action is sister to the dream'. I have swept away in the heart of the sea, at a depth of several fathoms, all my anxieties as a man. Worries of the moment, scientific curiosity, metaphysical doubts, have all been hurled into the sea and I do not regret any of them.

Like many others I do not feel in perfect harmony with our age and the solitude of diving lulls and stays a deep-rooted dissatisfaction. Down below, where dream and action move silently forward through the dense waters, side by side, man feels for a moment in tune with life.

Whether that is telling a story or not, I don't know. It is always possible to write an account of journeys on land. I have been from one end of Europe to the other and made almost a complete tour of Africa. Every country I have visited can be described: it is simply a question of landscape, people, distances. But for three years my life has been entangled in the life of the sea. The only period of my existence worth anything in all this time has been spent far from other men, beyond a curtain of crystal, with fish or underwater animals more foreign in appearance and habits than anything one might come across if one travelled to the ends of the earth. It has been an adventure without incident, and it is not yet over. Probably it will only end with my death. For those who have once listened to the siren-songs of the ocean-bed never return to land.

Norbert Casteret, in his Pyrenean caves, my friend Guy de Lavaur, exploring Padirac, have both had adventures with a quite definite beginning, middle, and end. You enter these subterranean grottos, you go all over them, and finally you leave them. The explorer may find a river, rooms, stalactites, narrow passages filled with clay, obstacles to surmount. . . . But once out in the open again he has only to relive his underground journey to make a tale of it.

But what am I to say, a sea-explorer whose objective is never reached, and who has never seen the end of those marine vaults, one minute black with shadows, the next hacked with swords of light? Here and there I have managed to snatch fragments of knowledge, I have tried to use my eyes and understand the meaning of what was before me, and to fit together where I could the pieces of a vague jig-saw of the sea.

But there is no need to organise expeditions to explore the sea. Anyone can go down when they want and come up where they want. All you need is a flask of compressed air, some goggles, a piece of lead round your waist. . . . Excuses are not so easy to justify, for we are each judge of our own daring, alone witness of our fears and hesitations. There are often humble and unimportant victories over ourselves. I have known bitter March mornings when the flesh refused to advance into a sea that cut like ice. I have shivered, alone on a rock, while the rising sun climbed behind the tip of the Islettes, simply because I was determined to observe the underwater world through all its seasons and because it seemed especially important to me at that green and yellow moment of the Mediterranean dawn. . . . But is that a 'story'? It's not even an anecdote.

Dramatic incidents? Certainly, I know a few; but I am not sure they can be described. Mostly they were trifling dramas that were over in a few seconds. A pipe getting hooked on to a piece of jagged rock; air-cylinders refusing to work in an underwater grotto; moments of animal panic when I couldn't wait to surface, desperate to see another human being. None of that is worth talking about and even Fargue, who perished at a depth of 60 fathoms, would probably have had nothing to tell if he had survived.

But divers do certainly have 'adventures'. Only they are not what landsmen usually understand by that word. The greatest, most exciting adventure is the mere act of being alive where, amongst men, only the drowned visit you. And of making yourself at home there, living a comfortable, peaceful existence.

Frederick II, one of the outstanding figures of the Middle Ages, Emperor of Germany, King of the Romans, King of Sicily and Jerusalem, and a great lover of the Mediterranean, one day indulged in a whim. He threw his golden goblet into the sea in order to encourage a diver to go down and look for it. Frederick hoped, by questioning the diver, to learn some new facts about the sea-bed. But it was a vain hope. The diver's account was bound to be useless: the sea's secrets cannot be picked up like golden goblets. The two or three minutes during which a man can hold his breath are not long enough to reveal a world. The undertaking is of an altogether different nature. It is by no means certain that our generation and the next one will even complete it. We can only make a beginning.

I have often thought about this king's curiosity. He was a man in advance of his time and in more than one way. I think I can guess what he was looking for and what the diver could not tell him. Frederick wanted to know whether this sea, in which simple fishermen let down their nets, was worth the interest of a prince such as himself: a philosopher, a man of liberal and daring intellect. The King of Jerusalem and Sicily was that day on the way to a great discovery. If his diver had not been blinded by the idea of the golden goblet, he would at least have been able to reveal one of the basic mysteries of the deep: that there is a visible frontier between the two worlds of earth and water.

'Sire', this man would have been able to say, 'at the depth which I was able to reach I only grazed the surface of whatever lay far beneath me; but at any rate I went through a screen, a veil of some kind, and that must mean something, for there was life of a sort going on there, too. . . .'

In fact one does not go straight into the sea. Between the air and the water a steel wave quivers. What people call the surface is also a ceiling: a looking-glass above, watered silk below. Nothing is torn on the way through. Only a few bubbles mark the diver's channel and behind him the frontier soon closes. But once the threshold is crossed, you can turn back slowly and look up: that dazzling screen is the border between two worlds, as clear to one as to the other. Behind the looking-glass the sky is made of water.

Is this light spilling out in all directions, this pure and deep substance, really water? So much brilliance and clarity does not seem to belong to the green, frothing surface, the glaucous and resilient element through which the swimmer has to strike his path. Once he has broken the surface, the diver who is properly ballasted has no more weight, no more resistance: an aerial softness transports him where he wills. Here the world is sweetness. There is not a place in his body, from head to foot, which is not relaxed. It is a pleasure to stretch out, to lie on one's back and feel the perfect fluency of one's muscles. Dreams float very slowly up from the sea. Walled in silence and completely alone, the diver begins an interior monologue in the cell of his undreamed-of content.

At a depth of two or three fathoms all swell subsides. Not a weed moves. A carpet of sand gleams faintly in the cleft of a rock some yards further down. A mysterious continent traces itself below me. I swim between the huge pages of an illuminated manuscript. Now I am dazzled by the purity of the light, the luminous beauty of the deep. A crystal quality in the atmosphere gives everything the cleanliness of a glass case. The opened pages end in a maze of rocks, beyond which a flow of blue water narrows out of sight and then widens. Over them is stretched a thick sky on which I glide until I reach shapes that turn underwater into peaks of the sea-bed, or cathedrals rising out of plains on summer mornings. Inspecting these summits, feeling the hard rock under their soft exterior of weed, gives one a respite before the final slide towards an invisible bottom. I swim round a sapphire steeple. Everything in front of me is blue, but if I look down a whole purple universe seems to swing out of the depths. Shall I go down to the foot of this tower or give it up on the way? At 20 fathoms, everything is forbidding, congealed, and cold, and the sudden iciness stabs me. I don't know whether it freezes or paralyses me: I feel it in me like a living thing, a disease. . . . What have I come here for? To explore the sea? I already know all that can be seen in it. I have come down in pursuit of a mirage. I have yielded to the dizzy madness of tearing open this blue canvas and making for the very heart of the dream. The Groupers, motionless in the shadow of their holes, gaze at the passer-by without stirring. Gorgonians spread their huge fans, quite still in the breathless water. Who has spoken of jungles? Not a single evasive flurry, not a moving shadow, brings this palace without walls to life. Were blood to flow, for example, it would not stain the crystal purity, for it would look blue. What is this vague terror from a Chamber of Horrors? The slightest rustle makes me tremble. I have even forgotten what the sky looks like, the real sky in which men can breathe without equipment.

Such is the aspect that submarine life presents, for the most part, to-day. twenty fathoms is a good limit, needing care but within reasonable bounds. Even ten years ago we were less daring.

If Jacques Bainville did not care greatly for history when he was a boy, I did not have much interest in sea-bathing. Swimming without any particular purpose has always seemed to me pleasant enough when it is hot, but it soon becomes boring.

Like many others I have done some underwater hunting. It was during the period of cross-bows with rubber stretchers and harpoons two yards long. But it was also the time when goggles first made their appearance. The submarine depths appeared in a new and staggering light. A few yards from the shore, their unsuspected lustre, their virginal beauty, were awaiting man's attention. So the most treasured memories of these early days are not of more or less successful attempts at harpooning. But, closing my eyes, I can fetch images out of a sea forever opening to my gaze; seaweeds of all kinds, grottos, dishevelled rocks, sun-dazzle twining its trellising along the sea-bed, and fishes that were strange or friendly and familiar. It was a world so rich and so inconsequentially revealed that I felt I was on the way to an important personal discovery. It seemed to me that the sudden annexation of such huge territories could not be without influence on my life.

Having succeeded in reaching the threshold I began to stumble. Goggles and tube enabled me, while remaining on the surface, to study the sea near the coast: idly pursuing fish that could scarcely escape, picking weeds at random, I indulged in undiscriminating wonder. But it seemed to me that there should be more to it than this, and I began to grow impatient. I was the guest at a party where I knew no one. It was irritating to see without understanding, to visit a country in which everything, animals, plants, even the way of breathing, was strange. I was like a Martian on earth.

It was then that I met Commander Philippe Tailliez. He was at that time in charge of the Under-sea Research Group, the scientific section of the Naval General Staff. And one day, in a little cove near Toulon, he sent me down with some bottles of compressed air on my back and made me bite the rubber tube: I breathed my first draughts of air. . . . The sea opened. I crossed through the looking-glass, no longer the ghastly, pallid body with the jerky gestures that fish and divers observe with some disgust splashing on the edge.

This underwater baptism, in the freshness of the spring sea, not only crowned me with riches that nobody could ever take away, but provided me with keys to unlock certain parts of myself. Drunk with the discovery of a new continent, I began at first to learn more about myself than about it.

Valéry has written a line in *Charmes*, in which, with the foresight of true genius, he expresses the very essence of what I felt:

*Heureux vos corps fondus, eaux planes et profondes!*

I was this *corps fondu*, the idealised but lively image of myself, and I moved in a landscape of dazzling reflections. The reverse side of the looking-glass was inhabited: fish, sea-weed, now at eye-level, offered me the extension of a reality for which I was not prepared. I felt one by one, like a kind of arthritis, my land origins. The mind was still less at home than the body. Freed of all anxieties about breathing, I moved around in the forbidden world. I was at least as much of a man in the water as I was on land: a man who could observe with discretion and no longer a wretch tortured by asphyxiation, blinded by splashes, going down a fathom or two only at the expense of great physical effort. The air was obedient to the call of my lungs. Everything became as simple as in a dream and this air which I breathed out climbed to the surface in great expanding bubbles, the supreme proofs of the miracle.

Lest anyone should misunderstand this story, let me repeat: I was a novice, a complete beginner. I have revisited the place of my first exploits: the depth of the cove is childish, but no act of daring to-day could ever give me so great a feeling of discovery, and of joy at wandering alone through a virginal forest and fashioning the sun into my own golden goblet.

On the rocks that day a family from Toulon was having lunch. It was a Sunday. I remember their loud voices, their amusement on the water's edge that anyone should bother to explore its depths. Were they aware, these Sunday revellers, that I was taking up all my promises to the sea and thanks to this second baptism renewing between man and the sea a contract broken 200,000,000 years ago? Did I even know myself?

Philippe Tailliez smiled at my enthusiasm. He didn't tell me that I had seen nothing and that I still had everything to learn. I discovered it for myself at my next dive. Then began a slow apprenticeship. To lose one's head over diving is only the beginning: the next step is knowing how to get the most benefit, once the sea has closed over you, out of this state of being a live, drowned man. One has to learn to be worthy of one's position as a 'melted body'. So a new life begins, with sterner pleasures.

The weight of our heredity, our whole past, dissuades us from accepting this sumptuous gift that the twentieth century offers us. Our ancestors, who lived in forests, have bequeathed us eyes that deceive us under water. Hunters have left us ears which are bad for diving and a sense of hearing which is useless in the sea. Accustomed for thousands of years to being warned, and to being able to avoid danger, by trusting to our eyes, our smell, our hearing, we are suddenly disarmed in an element where our horizon is limited to a few yards and where silence reigns. A fear born of ignorance keeps us company for a long time in this country, where we do not know how to distinguish dangerous from friendly creatures, plants from animals. We need this proof to be reminded of our ancient heritage, like those royal palaces one sees transformed into museums and which set the architect appalling problems. How many walls to knock down before we see the daylight, how many habits to renounce that we had taken to be the very marks of human intelligence: our idea of space, the hierarchy of our senses and the way to interpret their signals. . . . Our disturbed brain asks to be reassured by a gradual and careful approach to these new truths of the sea. And these new marine truths are in the process of becoming new human truths, for in future this apprenticeship to the deep will interest the masses. A large public, more numerous each year, tries to learn about the sea, about conditions that scholars scarcely understand. Biology, the study of marine plants, hydrography, all still the preserve of specialists, are becoming subjects of holiday discussion. Civil servants and housewives, as soon as summer comes, put on goggles to gaze into the waters and to sample an enchantment which ten years ago was reserved for initiates. For children the magic of the sea is as commonplace as television and radar. I am not one of those who deplore it. So immediate an intimacy suggests that the underwater world is less impenetrable than it seems. New discoveries are worked out, future activities planned: the last has not been said about the evolution of human life.

But the underwater world escapes the hands that clutch at it. The fish are not the only ones to disappear. A fathom down, in full daylight, everything is deceptive: the plant the diver was going to grasp is not where he saw it. He looks for his own hand and it is no longer where it was. Thus, even his body deceives and takes advantage of him below the surface. He has to start all over again, like a child in the cradle that fumbles awkwardly for its rattle and has not learnt to co-ordinate its movements with its instincts. That all comes. Soon enough.

To the observer in the water, looking through goggles or the window of a diving suit, an object four yards away seems only to be three. Rays passing from the water to the surface are refracted through the goggles: in fact the diver is looking at the sea through a magnifying glass. That in itself is sufficient to make life under water seem disconcertingly and deceptively enlarged. Not only are distances misleading but rocks and boulders, drawn near by the lens, appear unnaturally forbidding. I don't believe refraction to be the only reason for this. The diver's position and limits of vision are contributory causes. A man under water is not like a man standing up who can gauge the size of everything without distortion. Distances are diluted for him as he moves horizontally in his own length, and rocky peaks and walls rise up out of the mist to block the sky.

It was with a wreck, an old piece of gutted scrap-iron, that I came to realise this. I went down the first time using self-contained diving equipment and the decks, cluttered up with relics, seemed huge as I tried to wriggle between them. Wanting to examine the hull I went down again the next day, but this time I dived with helmet and tube. I was no longer self-contained, but instead I was able to retain something of a sense of proportion. I had a panoramic view of the wreck. Standing up in my heavy lead shoes, I could distinguish masts, the funnel, a winch. . . . We are made to see standing up.

But were we made for two or three dimensions? Length, breadth . . . but height as well? A climber's business, a pilot's, a bird's privilege, and a diver's too. He has four or five pounds of lead in his belt which curiously enough relieve him of some weight. Thus the landsman, riveted to the ground, and used to getting a stool to reach a shelf or take down a picture, is able, under the sea, to rise 15 or 20 yards with no effort at all. Equally, he can go down into the void, or rather what we call the 'void' on land, without worrying, for the void, a taut blue sky that breaks every fall, has no meaning in marine language.

Human weight: the jumper who has cleared the bar at between 6 and 7 feet is world champion. And with what an effort, with what twisting and contortions of a body in the peak of condition! Then it is a victory in which half an inch makes all the difference, while the underwater athlete seems to be borne by invisible wings. He can climb steeply and quickly, or gradually with gentle strokes, up an incline the very texture of a dream. There is nothing to get in the way of scaling or jumping, and flight and motion are controlled, at will, by sharp or gentle movements of the feet.

It is not true that the diver is like a fish in the sea. The fish has no lively reflexes; he is always on guard. Perhaps it will be understood if I say that he moves about the sea the way one flies in dreams.

It is here that psychologists should get to work. The Sorbonne should make plans and students of philosophy devote whole treatises to the study of the sea. We must not make a mess of the first stages of man's relationship to a new element. Experimental psychology should guide us through the traps laid on the sea-bed. I am thinking principally of the old problem of space about which our ideas are conditional and relative, and not fundamental. Guaranteed experience of marine dimensions, our relation to the outside world will never be the same again. The moment has come to revise our mental concepts, which have not altered since the origin of man. The whole process deserves closer study.

How can life be organised in a world without horizons? Perhaps we should start our inquiry with the inhabitants of those islands that are always wrapped in haze: the Lofoten Islands, Iceland. But is it a fog that floats through the great tanks of the sea? There is not a cloud, not a sleeve of mist. It is rather that one feels like an animal with short sight. Commander Rossignol has assured me that during a dive he has recognised a wreck at a 100 yards distance. For visibility of that kind there must be conditions of quite exceptional clarity. I admit I have never known them. On a very clear day in the Mediterranean you can see up to about 40 yards, though on 14th August, between 6 and 6.30 on a lovely evening, the wreck of the submarine *Vénus*, 15 fathoms down and 60 yards long, could be seen clearly from end to end. It was about three-quarters of a mile off the main dock at Toulon.

As a rule visibility is not more than 15 or 20 yards, and sometimes much less. Some light is diffused by particles suspended in the sea: so that an opaline curtain is hung before our eyes, whose thickness varies according to the nature of the sea-bed, the season of the year and the time of day.

The sun's rays reach as far down as the diver can go, to a

depth of 50 fathoms or more. William Beebe in his *bathysphere* only found total darkness at 300 fathoms. Light decreases in relation to depth, though it frequently happens that visibility is better at 8 or 10 fathoms than at 5. On certain days I have been able to take photographs which would have been ruined had I taken them 5 fathoms higher. They would have seemed 'blocked'. The plankton, even the dust, is thicker in the first strata of water. One often has to go through an apparent fog to reach clearer visibility lower down.

In the sea the sun's impact turns to heat by degrees. Its rays are absorbed, but not uniformly. The red disappear after the first few yards. The yellow, the blue, and the green are wiped out one by one. At 250 fathoms there are still enough violet rays to affect very sensitive photographic plates.

One might think that colours in the underwater world were of a monotonous similarity. But it is not so. If reds and yellows soon disappear from the diver's sight, greens of every shade, blues in their infinite variety, give each fish a distinct and individual character. The coral branch broken off at a depth of 15 fathoms may look blue, but it retains the gleaming polish and silky surface of coral. A glass-maker of genius has fused all the shades in the world into a stained window of one colour. And he has done it so faithfully, with such care over the subtlest shades, that it is possible to find red ingredients in its deep blue and to detect yellow in its cavernous green. You can easily verify this by diving with a watertight torch. In the beam of the white light plants and creatures assume their many colours, the useless colours that no one can see, the reds and yellows that a few volts are enough to summon up. Jacques-Yves Cousteau has made an underwater film in colour showing this transformation. At a depth of 15 fathoms a hand can be seen trailing a lamp. Pink seaweed surfaces out of the green depths and drops back into night. Gorgonians, caressed by the beams of this electric hand, raise golden palms on emerald trunks.

But how inadequate are all these words with which we try

to clothe a world beyond our reach: how feebly do these un-fathomable whirlpools, these terrifying abysses, correspond to the reality. Over this abyss man rests with calm confidence. It is neither the whirlpools nor the abysses that are frightening, nor the emptiness, but the rocks that pull you back, the laby-rinth that confuses you, the grotto and its shadows. Insignificant fears oppress us. Submarine topography is complicated: one gets lost in the sea like a child in a crowd. The wings of a black angel fluttered around me one day in the water off Cape Sicié where one of us almost died. Wandering from passage to passage, at the end of his tether and with no more air, dragged by a fierce current, he searched in vain for a way out of this ambush of sea and rock. Surfacing vertically, just where he could, he found himself 300 yards from his boat, exhausted, but in the reassuring, golden glow of a July evening. When we had hauled him on board, unloaded his equipment, and laid him on deck, he said he had had enough. It was a country too deep down for his taste.

Submarine countries are countries without shadow. Perhaps that is why we get so easily lost. The inadequacy of our senses, imperfect training in diving, are also factors, but the real reason is probably the absence of the sun. Ten or fifteen fathoms down all links with it are broken: we cannot estimate its whereabouts in the sky. Light comes from the very sub-stance of the water, so that neither seaweeds, rocks, fish nor our own bodies produce shadows, not even over the sand of underwater beaches. On land, even though it may be uncon-scious, we take constant bearings from the sun, thanks to shadows drawn upon the ground but rubbed out in the sea.

I have said that diving does not need organising like an expedition, with boat, chart, rope and sounding-rod. You need not always dive to the very bottom. These feats, satisfy-ing though they are, are costly and tiring. Only a difficult grotto, a wreck to explore, make them worth while. Too much equipment and preparation give to diving an extraordinary and pompous character which does not really suit it, for its essential quality, as long as one keeps within reasonable limits, is its freedom and easiness. Excursions along the coast, at a depth of 5 or 10 fathoms, can be equally interesting and rewarding. They involve familiarity with the sea, an ease and confidence, that are the signs of the real underwater traveller.

Round the whole French coast there are thousands and thousands of unknown sea-beds, new landscapes, waiting for their summer visitors. Some are muddy, without much character or charm, but many more are wonderful. The list will be filled in by degrees. Some of these regions, especially on the Mediterranean, are known about and have been photographed. The *Club Alpin sous-marin* in Cannes, the *Club de la Mer* at Juan-les-Pins, the Toulon *Groupe de Recherches sous-marines*, explore the coast and the islands round about, conquering on behalf of us all and annexing underwater territories to human life.

The *Club Alpin sous-marin* has given us 'Le Vengeur', as others have given us 'Le Cervin' and 'Mont-Blanc'. Le Vengeur is a sort of rough, sloping wall, off the eastern corner of Sainte-Marguerite, one of the Iles de Lérins, opposite Cannes. It begins, 5 fathoms down, with a large sun-warmed plateau, rich in plants and animals. This plateau, which is about a mile long, has one rocky peak about 40 yards high. The slopes of this constitute a biologist's showcase, a specimen market of life in all its aspects. Its craggy surface contains a series of ledges and holes that act as homes for numerous stationary animals. All those bearers of corollas, all those chalices festooned with tentacles, which early naturalists called 'animal plants' or 'animal flowers' collect there: sea-anemones, coral, ascidians, and the huge plumes of the most beautiful varieties of *Gorgonia*. Every yard of the way down is distinguished by a dazzling new specimen, every crevice, every archway, in the words of Dr. Deneréaz, is 'a Persian carpet in relief'.

That is only one side of life under the sea. There are plenty of others. As a contrast to the biological wealth of Le Vengeur, almost stifling in its luxuriance, one could mention the 'Cathedral of Notre-Dame', completely stripped of vegetation and without living creature. At Trayas there is a large underwater room whose only entrance is a narrow crack. Diving in this cave would resemble spelaeology if light did not ripple magically on to the water, if the rocks did not themselves seem to exude mysterious rays, and if the diver did not see a window opening to seaward out of its black walls.

At Cap Brun I know another cave whose water is not the summer-night blue of the Cathedral of Notre Dame. In mine the water is moon-coloured, the slightest movement on the diver's part makes pearls stream out of his body, and his breathing builds columns of diamonds.

My friend Georges Beuchat haunts the bays round Marseilles: Sormiou, Port Miou. . . . Along their rather monotonous coastline, barely marked by a few grey sand-dunes, he photographs animals shaped like dwarf palms. These are ordinary worms, tubicolous annelids called *Spirographis*. They live in tubes secreted by themselves, at the top of which they erect clusters of mauve, orange, and rainbow-coloured thread that were taken, for a long time, to be gills and whose main purpose is to provide a flow of nourishing water. Living in groups of two or three, the largest of them a foot or so long, they recall the child-like exoticism of a nursery mural. If the diver puts his hand out to touch them, they withdraw their plumes and all you can see are lines of headless stalks along the sand.

The list of underwater beaches worth a visit is already considerable: Cap Lardier, where large white flagstones form a superb stairway into the sea; off the Fourmigues, small islands opposite Giens, and a favourite diving ground of the U R G, there is a line of rocks 25 fathoms down on a bed of glittering sand and spangles; the islands off Hyères, which in ancient times were called the Stoechades and where they fished coral for export to Germany and India: Porquerolles, Port Gros, Levant. But the two smallest, and least accessible, are the most beautiful: Bagaud and le Roubaud. One day there will probably be a guide to the underwater beaches, with maps of caves, and descriptions of flora and fauna. We have not reached that stage yet; so let us take advantage of our privileges as explorers.

One has to resist the urge, in the sea as much as on land, to try to see everything at top speed and do nothing leisurely. This disturbing fever, which burns in the veins of generations of tourists, unfortunately upsets some of our diver friends.

An underwater site, even of poor quality, has many secrets to yield and probably one never discovers them all. It takes more than one visit to explore carefully. Not only because its passages, its mazes, its creeks cannot be easily explored, but because they vary at different times of the year, both in qualities of light and kinds of weed. Marine life cannot be studied at the rate of a conducted tour of the Château de Blois.

In this rich shrubbery of a world, where animals and plants, so closely related to each other, shy from man's gaze, life is not as haphazardly ordered as it seems. To a diver's eyes sea creatures do not mill about like passers-by in a street. Life under water could, without exaggeration, be called static, congealed in its luxuriant surroundings and secret retreats. Nor is it only coral, gorgonians, molluscs, sea-anemones, starfish, and other echinoderms who can be called the permanent residents of a particular site. Day after day, and from dive to dive, the same grouper and moray can be seen at the same hole, the same octopus lying in wait by its rocky hollow, the same group of sargues exercising in the same patch of sea.

As for the seaweeds, they seem to the beginner a confused mass in which he can scarcely distinguish shapes and colours; a tangle of foliage which must be handled and sorted to recognise the different kinds. The plant world is at its most exciting under water: only here there are draperies and hangings lining the rocks, rather than the 'carpets' dear to botanists. Their texture is so closely woven that the diver grazing this woolly cloak only notices a soft uniform surface like a field of grass.

Discovery of this kind of universe can only be made by degrees. The pace of underwater hunters in search of prey is too fast for anyone really wanting to get to know the sea. Many divers protest that they see nothing, because they are always on the move. The most exciting discoveries are reserved for those who can stay in one place for some time, compiling facts about all likely rocks and crevices. Pleasure in the submarine world is usually the reward for attention to detail.

The very technique of diving requires leisure. In an element eight times heavier than air exertion is tiring and nervousness extravagant. And if you get out of breath you use up a lot of air.

A restless temperament does not get the most out of miracles and life under water is composed of small miracles: the miracle of going down to lie on a bed of sand warmed, through the sea's density, by the heat of the sun; the miracle of going inch by inch over a sheer wall crammed with seaweeds, with the sea depths spread out like a blue sheet underneath; the miracle of coming unexpectedly on a narrow opening, a window cutting out to seaward a turquoise strip bejewelled with red plants.

When it comes to things like this, the diver has a great advantage over the underwater fisherman. The latter flies over a universe which he only enters now and then for quick glimpses. But the diver reaches slowly down to the heart of the waters. He has time to dream. There is, surely, a world of difference between looking down over a street from the fifth floor and sauntering on the pavement. The diver has the whole mansion of the sea at his disposal: with a flick of his feet he can cruise around it from the outside, go down to the basement, and then up to the first floor, like a deep-sea loafer.

So long as the eye can find something on which to focus, whether on rocky shelves or the sea-bed, these are harmless pleasures. But it is more dangerous in the open sea. The infinite, too, is a trap. 'The human mind', Bergson has written, 'feels at home when it is among inert objects, especially among the solid things which support us and provide us with tools for work.' In the flowing blueness of the sea, without landmarks, human intelligence does not feel at home and it sometimes shows it. Too much water bewilders and stifles it. There is a vast sameness that bores into the diver's eyes. A 'blue wall' springs up round him. His mind, like his eyes, shows signs of discomfort. He no longer knows where the sky is, or the seabed: like the airman, who, having flirted too long with the sky, loses touch with the ground. The diver looks vainly for landmarks, for signposts to show him the way to the surface. But the wall seems to close in on him, and there is nothing else to be seen except the confusing labyrinths of his own nightmare. His only chance is to keep cool and motionless, and to watch the rising bubbles of his own breath. That is the way to the surface, and he must follow the path of his breath if he wants to see the sun again and enjoy the reassuring familiarity of sky and horizon.

PLATE TWO above *The armchair diver. Diving man frees himself of his earthly weight*
below *Sunlight on the sea-bed*

PLATE THREE *Underwater view of the surface*

▲ A
B ▶
◀ C
D ▼

PLATE FOUR

A *Return to the surface. The Author wearing the Cousteau-Gagnan equipment*

B *The Swedish engineer Arne Zetterström trying out the hydrogen and oxygen mask in which he reached a depth of eighty fathoms. He died on his way up because of a mechanical breakdown on the surface*

C *The Cousteau-Gagnan self-contained diving gear*

D *The Author after diving with tube and helmet. This is the classical equipment, invented by Denayrouze and weighing 176 lbs.*

A  *A sting-ray. A poisonous spine under its tail makes it dangerous to*  PLATE FIVE
   *underwater swimmers*

B  *Head of a dying shark*

C  *A wounded grouper. Fishes suffer too*

D  *An octopus, dishevelled after handling*

PLATE SIX above *Diver surrounded by sea-bream*
below *The Author diving*

PLATE SEVEN *At the entrance to the 'Cathedral of Notre Dame'*

PLATE EIGHT above *A school of saupes: a kind of sea-bream*
     below *Sea-bream, the butterflies of the deep, at seventeen fathoms*
PLATE NINE *A grotto off Cap Brun*

PLATE TEN above *Remora, sea-pike and saw-fish*
below *Sharks are viviparous*

above Gorgonia *at the foot of* 'Le Vengeur'          PLATE ELEVEN
below *Tubicolous annelids on sand at five fathoms. The 'branches' are in
fact filaments that bring a current of nourishing water to the worm. Height
eight inches to one foot*

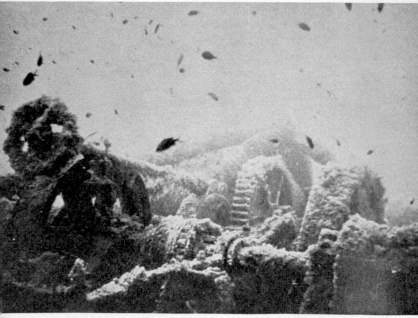

PLATE TWELVE above *Diver at eighteen fathoms*
below *Seaweeds gradually obliterating a wreck*

PLATE THIRTEEN *Pick work at Anthéor. Depth ten fathoms*

PLATE FOURTEEN above *Archæological research: a diver measuring ancient columns in the bay of Saint-Tropez*
below *An amphora, dating from the first century* BC, *found off Marseilles*

PLATE FIFTEEN *An amphora recently found at Anthéor*

# 2

# Conquest of the Deep

*If a man, completely under water, can hold his breath long enough and feed there, it seems clear to me that he will contrive in time to swim like the fish.*

ABBÉ DE LA CHAPELLE,
*Traité du Scaphandre*, 1775

THUS man thrusts his way underwater or, better still, walks there. I have just tried to describe his first impressions: that blue translucence, those landscapes created by rock plant and rock creature.

It will have taken thousands of years to win the battle against suffocation. There was no steady or continuous progress, no forward unbroken march towards the conquest of the underwater world. The very opposite. It seems that prehistoric man and classical man knew more about the depths and made better use of them than we do now. He had a more lively curiosity than we, the offspring of peasant stock diverted by the soil. The first migrations were all seaward. The sea was the earliest source of wealth, 'the country of the setting sun,' Professor Bertin wrote, 'the world of shells and cannibal fish which must have lured our distant forbears to the seaward trail.'

We still have the relics of their marine banquets. All over the world we come upon the leavings of those prehistoric feasts. Sometimes these deposits accumulate and form little heaps like the mounds at Saint-Michel en l'Herm (Vendée). They have been found on the shores of the North Sea, the Channel, the Bay of Biscay, the Mediterranean and the coasts of Portugal and North Africa. What are they made of? Shells piled on the beach, most of them are oysters and oysters are only found at certain depths. Even at low tide you cannot gather them on beaches. Scallops, which are almost as plentiful in these deposits, live in still deeper water.

It seems that prehistoric man groping his hard way through existence exploited the resources of the sea before he knew the way to use the soil. He depended for food as much on the fishes in the sea as on the beasts of the forests. He forged the same weapon against both: the spear. He fished and dived. He hunted for shellfish at least as much as he did for acorns or berries. The amazing Aurignacian civilisation preserved strange links with the sea; shells and even salmon bones have been found in burial grounds 100 miles inshore from the Atlantic and over 150 miles from the Mediterranean. Then the powerful tribes who peopled Brittany before the Celts— we do not even know their names—began the conquest of the sea. We find evidence in the Palaeolithic settlements at Pointe Saint-Mathieu, Cap Sizun and the hook of Penhoet. There is other evidence of mankind's marine past. In Normandy the remains of prehistoric ports, Sandouville, the promontory of La Roque, the site of Le Havre itself. Along the Mediterranean a whole chain of Ligurian harbours preceded the Greek and Norman settlements. From dim beginnings of human history some kind of marine activity emerges. Perhaps we have not paid enough attention to it. I purposely say 'marine' and not maritime. Montélius, Déchelette, Jullian and many others have shown the importance of sea traffic in those remote ages.

But I am dealing with the interest our ancestors took in the creatures of the sea, especially the ritual or the magical values that they set upon some of them. Our only documents, however, are a few sketches of fishes carved on bone and found in graves, perhaps adornments for some rite.

But we know much more about the civilisation that flourished in the Mediterranean for 1600 years, between 3000 and 1400 B C. The sea inspired the finest elements of the power, the best in all the art, of the Cretans.

By a stroke of fortune that seems to have resurrected the Aurignacian miracle more than 1500 years later, the Cretans harnessed land and sea to one great enterprise: the vase of Gournia with its octopus corresponds to the rustic procession on the vase of Haghia Triada. From the flying fish on the Phylacopi fresco to the bulls on the Vaphio goblet all their art emphasised the mastery of man over the creatures of land and sea.

Sailors? Of course. Fishermen? Certainly. But also divers. Cretan legend accords a special place to the hero who goes down into the deep, brings back its treasures and returns vested with the aura of divinity. The shells and pottery at Kouphonsi and Palaicastro prove that the Cretans knew about fishing for *Murex* and the extraction of its purple dye long before the Phoenicians.

It would be foolish to deny that they dived for sponges out of economic necessity rather than for pure love of deep-sea diving. But apart from such commercialism we may perhaps credit them with a knowledge and interest in the underwater world which we in the twentieth century might do well to imitate.

The octopuses, sea-urchins, conch shells and lobsters on their vases could only have been painted by great artists who had actually seen them in the sea alive. Cretan potters did not look on seaweeds or octopuses as lumps of jelly cast up by the waves, they visualised them in all the lively grace with which they drifted in the water. How many now can claim as much? Remember, too, those artists worked for people who never tired of marine paintings and who were certainly expert judges. For those pictures, even if designed for decoration, were scrupulously accurate. Both molluscs and fish, mullet, dolphin, parrot fish, are always recognisable.

Princes commissioned frescoes and golden goblets, merchants called for seals and cameos. Clearly they knew more about the sea and all that it contains in any Cretan workshop 4000 years ago than in the cities of the West to-day.

Phoenicians and the Greeks shared the Minoan heritage. Tyre and Sidon came into its sea-trade. Athens took over its terminology, its zest, its art and, above all, its great dream of establishing balance between the wealth of the sea and the fruitfulness of the soil. On the Acropolis at Athene's behest she paid homage to the olive tree, but she also honoured Thalassa, the deep sea. Among the Gods whom Crete bequeathed to Athens was the diver god. He symbolises the lure of the depths and the siren-song of the waves. He was called Glaucus. But the Greek myth is more discouraging than the Cretan legend. For one day Glaucus dived too deep and never came back. The old man of the sea received him into the company of underwater gods. Perhaps the diver's final defeat shows that Greek civilisation was less firmly founded on the seas than the Cretan.

The secret of Glaucus was a special seaweed. He only had to eat it for the sea to welcome him with open arms. But Greek divers, keen fishers of coral, mother of pearl and sponges, may well have known some more effective secret. Their naval warfare makes one think so.

Herodotus mentions a certain Scyllias of Scione and his daughter Cyana who was as skilled a diver as her father. During a storm they cut loose the Fleet of Xerxes from its moorings and then swam back five miles to join the Greeks off Cape Artemision, passing underneath the Persian keels. There is nothing impossible in that; Scyllias and his daughter could have come up to the surface from time to time for breath or used a leather respirator, or a reed, to take in air. These were the methods of the ancient divers. Scyllias and Cyana lived to see golden statues of themselves in the Temple of Delphi, though some time later Nero, moved either by love or greed, carried off the statue of Cyana.

William Beebe, the famous American ichthyologist, and the first man to dive 450 fathoms, has been keenly interested in the history of diving. He mentions in the short preface to his book, *450 Fathoms under the Sea*, that in the short account

Thucydides has left of the siege of Syracuse there is a reference to the Athenians sawing under water at the stakes of the Syracusan defences. Anyone who has tried to do the simplest work, even at one fathom, knows that you cannot use a saw under water without some sort of breathing apparatus. William Beebe concludes that the Athenians were equipped with 'something of the kind'. That is highly probable, though Thucydides does not mention it.

Aristotle, however, refers several times to underwater breathing gear, even describing the sicknesses and accidents to which divers were prone.

In his *Problems* he mentions an apparatus called *lebeta* which Alexander used to destroy underwater obstacles at the Siege of Tyre. *Lebeta* literally means cauldrons (lebes, lebetos) and the reference is probably to diving-bells. There is another passage in Aristotle which infers that the Greeks could swim a small way below the surface breathing through a pipe, probably a reed, the prototype of our divers' tubes. The passage begins: 'In the same way as divers use instruments to take in air from the surface so elephants have been endowed by nature with a trunk and when they swim across a stretch of water they lift it up and breathe through it'.

For a long time the most famous underwater feat was Alexander the Great's. All mediaeval tradition held that this great conqueror 'went down into the sea' and the chroniclers gave details. Alexander was supposed to have been accompanied by two friends, who took with them food and drink to celebrate, an activity he was never averse to. A glass cage was used so that he could look out at various fish and reptiles as they went by. One, in fact, was so long that it took four days and nights to pass the cage. This diving feat was an article of faith throughout the Middle Ages, a time, it must be admitted, of extreme ignorance about the sea.

The origin of this story is attributed to Callisthenes, nephew of Aristotle and Alexander's official historian. Greek scholars, however, point out that there is nothing of the kind in Callisthenes, nor in any of his contemporaries. It seems to be a landsman's fable, cooked up for peasants. But it would be equally rash to conclude that Alexander did no diving, for he was, beyond doubt, a brave man and a fine swimmer, as was proved by his crossing of the Hydaspes, when he was nearly drowned swimming 800 yards across the river at night.

His army is known to have contained detachments of divers, equipped with breathing apparatus, and Alexander, tamer of horses, must surely have tried the deep. But some such tale, passed from mouth to mouth through many centuries, may well have emerged in the form of the highly exaggerated story eventually picked up in Abyssinia by the man supposed to have been Callisthenes.

The Romans, like the Greeks, used swimmers in battle. They were called *Urinatores*, a term which has nothing to do with the little rubber bag divers carry down to-day to ease the bladder. The *Urinatores* were a corps entrusted with special missions and hand-to-hand attacks. They brought supplies in goatskins into blockaded ports, and carried orders written on lead armlets.

Most important of all, they destroyed enemy defences. But the adversaries of Rome began to devise countermeasures. They sank strands of wire strung with little bells, or lowered sharp-edged, wooden beams which spun round in the sea and wounded the Roman divers.

The equipment of the *Urinatores* certainly changed in the course of Roman history. The Romans, inheriting a naval tradition from Greece, made use of foreign specialists, both in their army and their navy. These crack troops appear to have been superbly fitted out. The best known of Latin military writers, Vegetius, who admittedly lived at a rather later period of Roman history, under Valentinian II at the end of the fourth century A D, refers to a diving suit in his *De Re Militari*; this was a hood with breathing tube attached, and another version, a bag made of gold-beater's skin, seems to have been a primitive draft of the compressed-air flasks used with our self-contained diving equipment.

Jal, in his *Archéologie Navale*, wrote: 'the famous *Urinatores* of classic times stayed under water for long spells with their mouths full of oil; this they dribbled out drop by drop'. Plutarch and Pliny have explained why: these divers had no underwater goggles and the oil helped them to see at great depths by lightening the density of the surrounding water. The Romans have often been called bad sailors, and they certainly owed a great deal to the Greeks, especially the Greeks in Provence, of whom Caesar made full use in his wars with the Veneti.

Yet these rather indifferent sailors had a real flair for marine biology, a feeling for fish. Fishponds and aquariums became fashionable in Roman society. Columella wrote an entire treatise on the way to manage a fishpond. Licinius Muraena, Quintus Hortensius, and Lucius Philippus seem much more ichthyologists than epicures. Quintus Hortensius bred fish in thousands, but he always bought the ones he ate at table in the market.

The Emperor Claudius achieved the most important feat of salt-water pisciculture ever attempted. He had a weakness for parrot fish, plentiful at that time in the Aegean, but rather scarce in the Western Mediterranean. He therefore had a great quantity caught, brought over in tanks, and then emptied into the sea off Ostia. For some time there was a ban on the catching, selling or eating of them in Italy, so that they could breed. Parrot fish caught to-day on the Italian coast and off Provence are only there because of Claudius.

A number of mosaics at Ostia, Naples and Sousa show how interested the Romans were in fish. At Volubilis, over 120 miles from the sea, an oil producer decorated his house with mosaics of Amphitrite surrounded by morays, dolphins and lobsters. This piece of snobbery on the part of an African merchant was a last eddy of the tradition that had spread, gradually dying, from Greece and the Aegean. The secret of the Tyrian purple was soon to be lost for 1500 years. All along the coast of Provence villages which had once looked on the sea turned their energies inland. 'The West lost its interest in the sea', Marc Bloch wrote. In future it was on land that peoples worked out their destiny, building up a kind of rural Christianity on the rustic legends of paganism. The man behind this civilisation was to be the peasant labourer bound to his plot of land by law, politics and faith. The Church, adopting the gods of springs and mountains, bestowed its blessings on the fields and filled the sea with fantastic and imaginary monsters.

In 1096 the Crusaders set out for Jerusalem, breaking down exhausted in Central Europe. Only a few Flemings thought of trying the sea route. Half a century later Louis VII was no nearer taking ship to the East. He followed Godefroy de Bouillon's tracks along the Danube, making for Serbia, Thrace, and Constantinople. By then the West European was no longer a simple peasant, he had become an infantryman or a horseman. The maps of Eratosthenes and Ptolemy had been lost; the New Europe was looking landwards.

Meanwhile Islam had taken possession of the Mediterranean and Ibn Khaldoun was soon to write: 'The Christians can no longer launch a single plank on the sea'. It was the Arabs who took over the traditions of the Greeks and Romans. Their divers, like the *Urinatores* using leather flasks filled with air, carried messages and even gold into Acre, under siege by the Crusaders.

I should perhaps develop or qualify some of these statements. But it would take too long to delve into the marine pasts of Marseilles, Pisa, Genoa, or Amalfi, whose interests were more concerned with sailing the sea than exploring it. The main fact is that the Middle Ages turned a maritime civilisation into a land one.

There is a picture in an illustrated edition of Vegetius' *De Re Militari*, dated 1536, showing the hood and tube apparatus mentioned a few pages back. Diego Ufano described something of the kind in detail a hundred years later. 'To improve diving conditions the Ancients invented a hood made from oiled cowskin. . . . It had horn eyepieces, and at the top there was a long tube'. Divers also used to put 'weights' on their feet. Ufano may not be quite accurate in attributing all this equipment to such early divers; the heavy boots and horn goggles at any rate seem to date from a later period. In any case this gear was only fit for shallow diving, not only because foul air soon chokes up a hood, but because the human body cannot breathe far below the surface. It was probably used for building quays and harbour works, rather than for underwater warfare.

Warrior swimmers in the Greek and Roman tradition distinguished themselves for the last time during the Turkish siege of Malta in 1565. After that superb feat of arms history had to wait for the British frogmen of 1940 to revive diving as a military weapon. The Vizir Mustapha, in his attack on Malta, sent down a squad of divers, armed with axes, to cut through a stockade that barred the harbour mouth. The Turks plunged into the water, but before they could reach the stockade they were attacked by Maltese divers. There was a ghastly underwater battle, which ended in the Maltese driving off the remaining Turks.

Despite the fame of this exploit throughout all Christendom, divers began to play a smaller and smaller part in warfare, and their reputation dwindled. The last divers to be officially recognised were those attached to the navy of Louis XIV; they were called 'Mourgons', but though they had the rank of officers, they were not used in war. Their duty was to inspect the keels of ships and supervise repairs done under water. The name 'Mourgon' is still used for a professional diver in the Mediterranean.

This is not a history of diving, many of which have been written, but a survey of the main stages in its development. We have now reached the end of the first phase, one in which diving was regarded as an art, especially a military art. It only remains to emphasise that at this period the sea was regarded as neither inaccessible nor terrifying.

These classic divers were descendants of pearl and sponge fishermen, inheritors of their technique. They could reach a depth of perhaps 10 fathoms, at most 20, and could stay a couple of minutes under water. The record stood in fact at 4 minutes 45 seconds, but it was in shallow water and without moving.

Perhaps they did breathing exercises before diving; nobody knows details of their training. We may one day unearth a treatise on the subject. We know for example that native divers in the Pacific breathe out when they reach the bottom as well as taking deep breaths before diving. Doing so, they follow ancient tradition. As a result they can stay much longer under water: carbonic gases are discharged and the blood takes in fresh oxygen. Recent experiments have tested the effect on divers of breathing pure oxygen for a minute or two before submerging: the dive can then last up to 15 minutes.

For three centuries, from the Siege of Malta in 1565 to Augustus Siebe's diving gear, invented in 1837, man's conquest of the deep made scarcely any progress.

The confused period that followed was marked by various experiments made with tubes and cauldrons, revivals of Greek *lebeta*. Its most interesting episodes, bordering on fantasy, were provided by eccentric diving machines which, luckily for their inventors, were never put to the test. A few names stand out above the chaos. There was, for instance, William Phipps, whose adventures figure in Marcel Schwob's *Imaginary Lives*. Phipps was a shoemaker's son who salvaged gold from a sunken ship off Haiti. He was knighted, became a rich man and was made Governor of Massachusetts. But in the end he lost both fortune and position, and died wretchedly in a London gaol.

Whatever historians may say, Phipps does not seem to have

used any diving gear of his own invention. It seems more likely that he relied on native divers. Anyhow the wreck lay in shallow water. Halley's story is more interesting. He was an astronomer, interested in the sea, and used the traditional diving bell. His invention was a gadget that renewed the diver's air supply. It provided him with empty barrels linked by tubes to the bell. When the barrels were opened the pressure of the water drove the air into the bell. Halley went even further, fitting a wooden helmet to the diver's head and linking it through a pipe with the air-filled tub. It was, in fact, the first attempt at a diving suit.

So far there had been no scientific basis for underwater experiment. Only Archimedes came near to finding one. Halley (1656–1742), Torricelli (1608–47), Pascal (1623–62) and Denis Papin (1647–1714) all contributed something. Their example was later to inspire the German scientist Klingert, who, in the Oder on 23rd June, 1797, tried out with some success a diving suit with bellows. He perfected this apparatus, adding to it an air-tank, compressed by the force of the water, enabling the depth to be controlled. This is, in essence, the principle of the modern diving suit. Its materials show how the inventors' minds worked. Klingert was the first to use a tin helmet, but it was a crude affair. For centuries inventors had been experimenting with cauldrons which capsized under water, barrels apt to burst, and leather tubes smeared with bees-wax, that let out air. Before these odd contrivances could be replaced, industry had to provide copper, steel and especially rubber.

Now Augustus Siebe had his chance. Born in Saxony in 1788 he died in London in 1872. He fought at Waterloo as an artillery officer in Bluecher's army, and settled in England soon after. His interests and his mechanical genius had many sides. Clockwork, paper-making, valves, electric appliances, even a machine to register the height and weight of army recruits, which was bought by the British Government and used in the Crimean War.

In 1819 Augustus Siebe made his first diving suit, a small metal helmet with a tunic down to the hips. The air pumped down from the surface escaped at the belt. In 1837 he completed a strong, simply made device on the principles in use to-day. It consisted of a water-tight suit and removable helmet with intake and outlet valves. It was adopted by both the British and French navies, a privilege enjoyed by the firm of Siebe (now Siebe Gorman & Co.) until 1857.

Although he never perfected it, Cabirol, a Frenchman, did useful work in making the public familiar with this new kind of apparatus. He was a southerner from Narbonne, a tireless demonstrator, a keen collector of medals and awards. He took advantage of the Paris Exhibition of 1855 to make several dives into the Seine before a large crowd which included Prince Napoleon, cousin to the Emperor. Cabirol's services should not be underestimated for, thanks to him, the diving suit came into general use and a convict at Toulon was able to reach a depth of 20 fathoms.

Two Frenchmen, a mining engineer called Rouquayrol and Lieutenant de Vaisseau Denayrouze, invented various improvements, adding a pressure regulator and an air-tank, making divers virtually independent. But there was still much to do. Man admittedly had made the legend of Glaucus and the fable of Alexander plausible; now he could really dive, even though he often paid for it with his life. It became apparent that it was not enough to provide means of breathing for a diver to survive under water.

Diving suits soon became more common, so, too, did 'diving bells'. At the close of the nineteenth century there was a craze for public works, and many imposing new buildings, such as quays, bridges and lighthouses, had underwater foundations. Engineers working on them made diving bells in which compressed air offset the pressure of the water.

Yet workmen were still suffering from complaints and mishaps already observed in divers. There was a vocational

disease: 'bends' or caisson disease. The illness which sometimes began with simple itching could also cause trouble in
the muscles and joints, swellings, nervous disorders and
paralysis. Some never recovered, others died suddenly for no
obvious reason. Doctors, failing in diagnosis, inclined to put
it all down to cold and damp.

Paul Bert (1833–86), the French physiologist, must be
given credit for offering a scientific explanation. He showed
through comparative study of conditions at high and low
pressures, the relationship between diving sickness and air
sickness; for, between 1870 and 1900, man was simultaneously experimenting in both air and water. Paul Bert's two
books *Leçons sur la Physiologie comparée de la respiration* (1870)
and *La Pression Barométrique* (1878) demonstrated how in
both cases nitrogen, slow to react to changes of pressure,
forms bubbles that clog the circulation of the blood.

It is hard to understand why people were so slow to accept
such elementary and vital principles. Diving sickness and air
sickness still claimed their victims, and what's more, scientist-
victims. On 15th April, 1875 – five years after the publica-
tion of Paul Bert's *Leçons* – three aeronauts, Crocé Spinelli,
Gaston Tissandier, and Georges Sivel, set out to explore the
upper layers of the atmosphere on the balloon *Zenith*, reaching a height of 27,000 feet. Tissandier, as they came down,
emerged from a deep coma to find his two friends dead.
Paul Bert is said to have warned them, but in vain, about the
consequences. Feeling in France at the time ran high. The two
victims were regarded as 'sacrifices to Science'. To tell the
truth they died largely because they refused to listen to Bert.
Their coffins were followed by 20,000 people, and a tomb
was built by public subscription at Père-Lachaise.

Paul Bert was in contact with Siebe in London. His theories
must have been better received over there, for in England the
work begun by the Frenchman was later developed by
J. B. S. Haldane and his colleagues. Their efforts culminated
in the system of 'gradual decompression' (1906) and in the

drawing up of a 'de-compression table'. The English acquired, as a result of this, an uncontested supremacy in deep-sea diving.

The diver, bound by his tube and his rope, a captive-diver in fact, was still far from cutting a figure. A contemporary handbook, speaking of diving precautions, says that a diver 'should be as carefully protected as a child in leading-strings'.

This child was soon to cut the leading-strings; not at first for his own convenience, but to save human life. For years every effort was to be made to give the crews of submarines a means of escape, as disasters like those of the *Farfadet* and the *Lutin* had deeply stirred public opinion.

We have seen how Rouquayrol and Denayrouze converted Siebe and Cabirol's diving suit into a self-contained apparatus by replacing the pump with a compressed-air tank strapped to the diver's back. But they still kept the orthodox helmet, general attire, and lead shoes. Diving equipment that took so long to put on was obviously unsuitable for the rescue of submariners. A trial period produced something lighter, but still imperfect. For instance, Boutan's Apparatus, adopted for a short period by the French Navy.

In 1915 Sir Robert Davis made vital improvements with his 'Submarine Escape Apparatus', dispensing with the suit and lead shoes. A bottle of highly compressed oxygen opens into a bag through a tap worked by the diver. He holds in his teeth a device through which he inhales oxygen and exhales carbon dioxide, purified by a special filter, before being returned to the bag.

But this technical progress still did not open the gates to the underwater world. Psychology at this stage had a part to play as well as industry. True, a new type of diver appeared, thanks to Sir Robert Davis, who had little in common with Siebe and Cabirol's brain-child. He was no longer an infant in 'leading-strings', treading the ocean bed as if on eggs, but a lithe swimmer circling horizontally under water. But, despite its exceptional scope, this sort of diving was still considered risky. Submariners using this equipment never dreamed of exploring the sea-bed. The problem was a practical one: how could the crew of a sunken ship best surface through waters of varying density? This equipment was always tried out along similar lines. The submarine was sent down about 5 fathoms. Then one by one the crew, provided with masks, were let through a kind of 'lock', trying, on emerging, to control the rate at which they surfaced. A boat was waiting to pick them up.

There was no temptation in such circumstances to stop on the way and study oceanography. Submariners had, like that, no clearer conception of the sea around them than from the steel hulls of their boats. Before their diving goggles there passed the same pale green water as streamed over the lens of their periscope.

Commandant Le Prieur reconceived the purpose of diving equipment. He saw that it might be used for going into the sea rather than simply for escaping from it as quickly as possible. He may have seen the journey as a downward one because he was no submariner. It was a decisive point. For from the very beginning of his naval career he was required to dive: in 1905, as a midshipman in the *Dupetit Thouars*, serving in the China Seas, he had to survey a wreck, and, two years later, in the *D'Entrecasteaux*, to go down and free a propeller. After that he dreamed constantly of some simple device for shallow diving.

In 1925 Commandant Le Prieur invented the first self-contained diving gear, perfecting it in 1933. It consisted of a compressed-air cylinder, a diver's mask, and a reducing valve. The compressed air allowed stays of 20 minutes under water at about 25 feet and of a quarter of an hour at 36 feet. The novelty of this system was that the diver no longer had to breathe through a closed circuit: the foul air was not, as in the Boulton and Davis gear, purified by an unreliable filter; it escaped into the water under the edge of the mask. One of the risks of diving, suffocation by carbon dioxide, was eliminated. Another advantage: it used compressed air instead of oxygen, which is dangerous at high pressures.

In 1935 Commandant de Corlieu added rubber paddles, used to-day by explorers under water and in future indispensable to divers.

In 1943 the self-contained apparatus evolved by Lieutenant de Vaisseau Jacques-Yves Cousteau and an engineer named Gagnan was successfully tried out. This apparatus, which has now been adopted by the French Navy and which makes descents to over 300 feet, was simpler and more robust than that of Commandant Le Prieur and its various modifications. In particular, it included a reducing valve that released air as required, no matter what the position of the diver, while the mask was replaced by a simple pair of underwater goggles.

Finally, in 1944, the French Navy established an Undersea Research Group, putting it under the control of the General Staff. This was at the instance of Commandant Cousteau and Capitaine de Corvette Philippe Tailliez, both of whom had been involved, since 1938, with the problems of diving.

Thus, after much research and experiment, the French caught up with the work done in England, and by the Germans during the Occupation at their experimental station at Carnac.

The last war brought about great improvements. After 2000 years *Urinatores* reappeared. They were equipped in Italy and Germany, as well as in England, with gear based on the Davis Submarine Escape Apparatus. It fulfilled the great essential: unobtrusiveness. But its one great drawback was that even at small depths the diver was liable to suffocation. The British consequently set a limit of four fathoms on their frogmen. British 'frogmen', Italian 'nautatori', German and Japanese divers carried out many daring exploits, not yet recorded. British frogmen won great renown on the Rhine and Oder crossings during the German retreat. The nautatori, picking their way through the defences of Gibraltar, Alexandria and Algiers, inflicted serious damage on English warships besides sinking tankers and cargo boats. The Japanese divers were instrumental in the taking of Hong Kong. The Germans themselves used divers at Nijmegen. A new type of fighting man, the human submarine, had arrived. Single-handed or in a midget submarine he attached delayed-action bombs to the hulls of warships or blew up enemy defences just as in the time of Alexander the Great.

In the old-fashioned diving suit, man remained a prisoner. He was a landsman at the mercy of artificial, cumbersome devices: he could not move freely, nor without intensive and expensive training, and he depended ultimately on others.

To-day the diver is in a happier position: he can dress himself unaided, dive and surface as he wishes. The compressed-air cylinders on his back enable him to stay under water for as long as an hour at five fathoms, or forty minutes at fifteen fathoms. He wears fins on his feet, and goggles, instead of lead shoes and a copper helmet. Light weights on his belt help him to find his own trim, as necessary for a man as for a submarine. He can float horizontally instead of being forced to remain stiffly upright. After a little training he can rely entirely on his fins for moving, so that his hands are free to pick specimens or take photographs.

The diving apparatus now at our command is more than an improvement, it is in fact an instrument of discovery rather than equipment; an instrument devised to eke out the strength and endurance of men. Thus the hoe, 8000 years ago, opened the vegetable world to man. The underwater world lies within reach. Michelet begins his rather uneven book, *La Mer*, 'Man cannot live in the sea. It suffocates him. There will always be that eternal barrier between the two worlds.' Prophecy is rash. The eternal barrier has been broken down, and not by man alone. Philippe Tailliez trained his dog to dive, building a special suit for him. This dog, following his master into the heart of the sea, has symbolic value: it marks the extent of our technical powers.

But though we may possess the means we have not exploited them. In the middle of the twentieth century the sea is still unknown. The two worlds are in touch, yet as fundamentally separate as in Michelet's day.

From Pole to Pole every sea has been sailed, sounded and christened. The International Hydrographic Institute has listed 48 names, but they are surface names. Under every keel, beyond the side of every ship, the waters keep their secret. Crossings are not explorations, and man has only sailed surfaces bleak and barren as a desert. He has not worried about what was underneath. No sailor has yet made anything on the sea, not even a garden of seaweed.

Navigators have learnt to recognise winds and stars. They have more understanding of the sky than of the sea: the sky with its storms, typhoons, and aircraft. But not the seaweed valleys with their underwater plants and fish.

We must now start moving downwards. For the portion of the world on which we live is small. The earth's surface is 196,940,000 square miles, approximately 55,063,000 square miles of land and 141,877,000 square miles of water. We only use a quarter of it. Hemmed in by our narrow surroundings we never look beyond them. The villager is limited to his village, the peasant to his soil. On that soil man has measured out his fields, built his home and based his whole outlook, without reflecting that beyond his horizon there are great unknown stretches of water. It is time to remeasure the earth. In depth.

Man's exploitation of the sea has only just begun. Divers have done little more than point out a few caves and reefs. We are groping round the rim of a great basin. But our first duty is clear; the exploration of the 'continental shelf'. Every continent is extended by a projecting shelf, sloping gradually from low water mark to about 600 feet: this, geographers call the continental shelf. At its edge there is a precipitous drop, and the sea suddenly becomes much deeper. In the days of sailing ships this was called 'blue water'. There, depths of 1000 fathoms and more begin.

The continental shelves stretch for 170,000 miles, with an overall surface area of about 8 million square miles. With their deep underwater valleys and rocky precipices, they are mysterious, unexplored landscapes. The Seine, for instance, doubling round the Cotentin Peninsula, where it receives as tributaries the Rance, Elorn and Avon, follows the continental shelf and only 'disappears' into the sea off the Petite Sole bank. Several underwater canyons have been found off Provence, the largest at Banyuls, Cassidaigne, Sicié, Toulon and Porquerolles.

The continental shelf, with its gentle slope, is man's best approach to 'civilising' the sea, exploring its bed, taming its creatures, cultivating its vegetation. Fish use it as spawning ground, and the sun's rays reach down to it. The seasons irradiate it, bringing their autumnal deposits and their spring champagne. It is the biological antechamber to the ocean, and will probably be the base for our next operations. But we are still treading cautiously on the threshold of the 'promised sea'. No diver has so far reached the 100 fathoms that mark its boundaries.

The main obstacle is drunkenness, the 'rapture of the deep seas'. It affects different people at different depths. It has been observed at 15 but is more usual at 30 fathoms. Some exceptional divers have only felt it at 50 fathoms. A man becomes aware of great sleepiness, a sense of euphoria that breaks down his resistance, making him welcome death and acclaim suffocation. No myth has ever equalled the tragic grandeur of this scientific truth. When he made his fatal dive in 1947 Fargues, of the URG, fell victim to this intoxication of the deep seas. As he went down he made scratches on pieces of slate attached to an anchored rope. The last mark he left was at 60 fathoms.

To guard against this danger, it seems that divers ought to be supplied with some kind of mask in which nitrogen would be replaced by a non-anaesthetic gas. The Americans use a mixture of helium and oxygen for deep-sea diving. But helium, produced in fair quantities by American industry, is expensive in Europe, too dear for everyday use. The Swedish engineer, Arne Zetterström, used a mixture of oxygen and hydrogen in a special diving suit of his own invention. On 7th August, 1945, he reached a depth of 80 fathoms in the Baltic. He was working in conjunction with the Swedish naval ship, *Belos*, in the Gulf of Landsort at the extreme southern end of the Stockholm Archipelago. But faulty handling of the raising gear caused him to be hoisted straight up from 25 fathoms. He lost consciousness and died soon after reaching the surface. He was only 28 and had already touched a depth of 56 fathoms in 1944. An Englishman, William Bollard, however, still holds the world record in open water. In August 1948 he exceeded 81 fathoms.

To reach 400 fathoms man has still to fall back on diving machines, as in Halley's time. A prisoner in a ball of steel like William Beebe in his *bathysphere*, or Otis Barton in his *benthoscope*, he can only, though at a depth of 450 or 600 fathoms, peer out through quartz scuttles. In the icy darkness he makes out nightmare creatures; reptile heads with long, hooked teeth and rope-like bodies, open jaws swollen with monstrous arborescent growths. These creatures are luminous, their light appearing at the end of a stalk like a lantern on a stick, or else like the headlights of a car.

Down here the conquest of the deep is still only a tentative reconnaissance. Our descents seem contemptible compared with the mean depth of the sea, 2000 fathoms, and still more so, with the greatest known depth, 5500 fathoms. William Beebe, in thirty-three dives, only twice got further than 300 fathoms. In 1949 Otis Barton touched 685 fathoms. But limited in their movements as they both were, at the mercy of a cable, what they saw of the sea-bed could not be much. All we really know of deep seas comes from dredging and sounding. For the rest we fish in darkness, and the secrets of the abyss elude us.

There is, however, Professor Piccard, whose thirst for records having been satisfied in the stratosphere, now wants to provide scientists with the means for underwater exploration. And, it must be admitted, he and his assistant Max Cosyns, despite a preliminary setback, have succeeded. The *Bathyscaphe* seems to meet the needs of the future. It is a dirigible balloon, not even linked with the surface. Petrol replaces gas. An electric engine, driving a propeller, enables it to travel about $12\frac{1}{2}$ miles under water.

The experiment made in 1948 off the Cape Verde Islands was not entirely satisfactory. Certain technical faults showed it to be imperfectly adapted to underwater conditions. But it still went down, without passengers, to 690 fathoms, and has obvious potentialities.

From the fisheries of prehistoric man to modern underwater explorers, from the Greek *lebeta* to Piccard's *Bathyscaphe*, from the diving suit of Vegetius to the Cousteau-Gagnan device, the whole history of diving seems like a long series of preparatory attempts, leading to man's eventual mastery of the sea.

We have conquered the air, even the stratosphere, and we can travel through them. But we have only skimmed the upper layers of a world three times the size of ours. There are ocean wastes hiding a secret civilisation, to which men may one day find their way. Biologists, geologists and physicists will survey its canyons, classify its unknown life, and explore its possibilities.

# 3

# Sea-Meetings

*On the whole fishes are more intelligent than they are supposed to be.*
LEON BERTIN

To the swimmer clear water alone is reassuring, and man's mistrust has always been awakened by sharp and concealing corners or slopes too rich in vegetation. Throughout history the best divers have come from the clear-water countries, Greeks, Italians, Polynesians. Bretons, who are such good fishermen, never dive and seldom even swim.

Our anxiety in the water is like a blind man's, but by wearing a diving mask we enjoy clear vision and can get rid of the phantoms. Yet there remains in all of us a more or less vivid memory of those legends which peopled the sea with monsters and shadowy catastrophes.

All these underwater terrors have not yet been dispelled. How many times have I seen a friend tremble when I touched him on the shoulder under water and he had not felt my approach, how many times have I not shuddered as something brushed against me! Our imagination goes on suspecting mysterious dangers, where in reality there is only a dark patch or a harmless creature more frightened than we are.

Fear, cruelty, incomprehension leave a heavy mark on our first encounters with the water world. We go into the sea with all our landsman's prejudices. On land we participate in a hierarchy of emotions which excludes the sea creatures; the man who can't bear to see a rabbit killed will look on with a cold eye while the back of a live fish's throat is torn out with the hook which is caught in it. The death-agony of all terrestrial things, from a horse to a hedgehog, wakes in us some feelings of sympathy and egotism, some echoes of tenderness for the common fate of beast and man. This sense of pity which is so easily aroused remains indifferent to sea creatures; our clemency is unable to go further than the shore or to be extended to the living world beyond.

Yet life and death are the same on land and sea; the blood which flows there is just as red, and in its farewell to life the flesh of the scalebearers should offer as pathetic a spectacle to our eyes as that which is covered by feathers or fur. But far from it: a fish to most of us is generally only an oblong sack of bones and scales. If it dies in convulsions it dies at any rate in silence and makes a nice clean corpse with a minimum of blood and gut. So we conclude it feels nothing.

That is because we watch it die in the air; once on land, where it is so helpless, a fish loses even the means to express suffering. It's quite a different thing when the death-throes take place in the water. The eye-witness soon finds that he is spectator of a drama as painful as that of the dying hind which tramples on its entrails. The true hunter's instinct is the same in both cases. To finish them off quickly. If this seems hard to believe, here is the opinion of an underwater fisherman, Bernard Gorsky, from his *Dix Mètres sous la Mer*.

> I shall always have a clear memory of a splendid specimen of over five pounds which I harpooned with a horizontal shot. In its struggle the drum-fish tore itself free and disappeared in a large overhanging crevice. I reloaded and was about to go down again when the fish reappeared, completely disabled; unable to turn it was coming up towards me, dragging its pale intestines; there was such an anguish in the position of the body, in the expression of the half-closed eyes that I was frozen by it and it was with very mixed feelings that I fired my harpoon again.

For the first time in human history man and fish are finding themselves face to face in the same water, breasting the same weed. I can remember the time when fish were less frightened for their lives and would come up to nose my harpoon. Now their education is complete, they know we are murderers and flee at sight. I believe we have missed a wonderful opportunity, a possible friendliness such as the birds gave to Saint Francis. For fishes holiness wasn't even a requisite!

Let us confess; we have gone down into the sea, into this unlooted palace, with the mentality of the line-fisherman. In this world under water we might have become, not a feared and hated spoil-sport, but an understanding witness and a tolerated guest. For that we should have had to grasp the fact that fish were receptive to communication, that they could be tamed and perhaps one day domesticated. These discoveries we owe to the self-contained diving apparatus, to this instrument for increasing knowledge which has come too late. Yet the harm done is not irreparable.

The ancient naturalists, who did not claim to know everything and had fewer books to consult than our contemporaries, laid the greatest stress on the direct observance of nature in their instructions. They recommended keeping quite still in a field or a wood in the full knowledge that wild life will soon make its appearance at any spot that seems uninhabited. It is an experience still worth trying in the water-world. A little patience, a studied immobility, a smoothness of gesture, and some part of the animal world will regain confidence—but only a section of it. For the larger denizens, at any rate on our own coasts, I am afraid all hope has gone.

A diver can explore the projecting cliff-face which no net can ever get to, he can examine the sea-bottom which no apparatus can reach—at least a third of the Bay of Morlaix in Brittany is impossible to drag. And one might quote innumerable examples. It is in these grottos and along these rocky corridors that it is still possible, with a little practice, to surprise the 'wild life' of the sea. To visit these depths, as the diver will soon find out, is to become a collector of oases, each of them with its own inhabitants, climate and regulations. There is a photograph by my friend H. Broussard that shows a diver nearing the sea-bed and covered with fish almost as though

they were confetti. This picture evokes the happiest memories
for me, for I am far too lukewarm a hunter to get excited by
pursuing a drum-fish or attacking a grouper. My happiness is
derived from gliding down in the clear light towards a shoal
of motionless fish or allowing a tightly packed procession of
grey mullet to file by above my head. It is in October or May
that such little miracles usually take place. There are some
lucky days and fortunate rendezvous when fish grouped
according to their kind cross and recross each other and pay
no attention to man. The diver takes up his position in a
roundabout of sparkling scales, a silent and motionless on-
looker whose least movement would ruin everything. These
days are as rare in the sea as some kinds of spring morning in
the country, days when the transparency of the water corresponds to the sweetness of the air above and when the joy of
living reaches to 5 fathoms below the surface.

To grasp the full riches of the underwater world there's no
need to explore the Caribbean with its parrot fishes and coral
scenery. Along our own shores, whether on the Mediterranean or the Atlantic, there's hardly an islet, a reef or a cove
without enough vegetable and animal life to surprise and
delight us. But of all those oases the most beautiful are sunken
wrecks. Bearded with seaweed, home of shellfish and octopus,
quivering with fishes, they attract life and bring it to comple-
tion. In the end one comes round to the idea that these rusty
plates of steel offer to sea creatures an irresistible attraction or a
certain wry pleasure. The explanation may be that most fishes
do not require a hiding-place or a bolt-hole so much as a
labyrinth; they love to be in possession of several safety exits
and have a weakness as well for the winding channels which
form round a wreck and which provide an equal proportion
of light and shade.

These ghostly vessels, for ever dead to human eyes, vibrate
with underwater life and become the scene of innumerable
games and fights and lyings-in. Yet when we get to them,

between 20 and 25 fathoms down, an absolute calm seems to reign. We have to give everything a second look and undertake an inspection which may require some courage. Slowly the boat comes to life, some brusque departure traces a line of silver through the shadow, a great moray's head appears and moves from side to side, emerging from the dark to inspect a square yard of blue water, at the entry to the lower-deck an octopus blows itself up, undecided between boldness and retreat.

Some wrecks have become the sole property of one tyrannical species; there are boats taken over by the moray and others by the octopus and there are immovable creatures which also taste the joys of empire. There is an old Greek cargo boat, sunk in the Mediterranean for some thirty years, which has been invaded by a sea-moss, 'Neptune's lace', with fine crimped petals pierced by tiny holes. The masts are covered with them, and when we examine them closely they suggest those ivory ships which they used to carve at Dieppe and which turned yellow under their glass cases. An ascidian, *Phallusia mamillata*, has taken possession of *La Galissonière* which sank in Toulon harbour.

Round these hulks there sometimes stretches a desert of mud, flat sands without an undulation or a single weed. We may carry out a gloomy survey of such areas without encountering a single living creature. This adds to the surprise when we reach the oasis, for as we approach the hull and lay hold of the weed-encrusted hand-rail, a flock of sargues, those fork-tailed sea-bream, takes flight. It seems that these dead ships are able to nourish these forms of life from their corpses.

Whether because of the exceptional luxuriance of life round a wreck or the more usual biological paraphernalia on sunken rocks, the stroller under water will not fail to be aware of the shape and reactions of the creatures he discovers. A host of questions begins to haunt him and demands some kind of answer.

For a thousand years man has been in contact with land animals whose character and habits have been deformed by domestication. He has ended by believing that he understands them. All he means by that is that he is able to rely on certain reflex actions which he himself has implanted in them. He will flatter himself at times on a grasp of animal psychology which has brought him the love of the dog and the purr of the cat. It is in the strength of such assumptions that he approaches the beasts of the sea.

A fish swims slowly past him, paying no attention. It's an animal. Like all the others? Surely its watery surroundings, which impose such peculiar conditions, will have given it some quality of uniqueness in the animal kingdom? Does the diver who quietly shadows a fish know any more about it than it does of him?

What is life like in an incompressible liquid? How much can one see? What is the nature of our sufferings? What forms the basis of a fish's fears and joys? If we can believe our own observations, the diver first tries to understand the nature of the sensations of the beast he follows. He would like to know what frightens it and how to attract and reassure it. He experiences the temptation to behave as in a farmyard and to try out the gestures which bring the hens round him or which calm frightened children. Don't laugh at this—at least he credits fishes with a faculty of intuition and a certain richness of sensation. It's not a false hypothesis.

Those who now know fishes better through having hunted them or observed them in their own element no longer underestimate them. They know how to distinguish degrees of intelligence, not only in the different kinds but among individuals of the same species. They have found some to be wily, others simple, and, as it were, unawakened.

A sea–dace which is being chased keeps its distance but never seems in a hurry, it knows where it is going and works out the tactics which it will employ to get out of a bad spot. It will guide the hunter to a maze of rocks which it knows well and then suddenly dive into the full shadow, rest motionless in a cleft for a moment and sail peacefully out by a hole opposite where it went in. The duped hunter is still waiting for it when it is already far away. All anecdotes of underwater fishing prove one fact only—and how important it is—that a fish, when its life is in danger, does not only use the physical qualities with which Nature has endowed it but its brain as well.

According to naturalists fish are in possession of four senses —taste, hearing, sight and sensitivity to vibration. These are landsmen's words, and to get nearer the truth we must transpose them into the world of water. Anyone who has lived in long familiarity with this will know that sensory perceptions cannot be enclosed in such rigid terms. However at a loss our senses may be when we dive, they still send out a whole range of subtle signals which we have hardly the terminology to express, and yet we claim to be able to define the perceptions of a creature gifted with senses which we lack completely! The lightness, viscosity, fluidity, resistance, buoyancy and salinity of the water are for us sensations which engender discomfort or pleasure. There where man, an animal whose temperature is constant, is sensitive to the warmth of the water, what must be the sensations of a fish whose temperature varies with that of the sea? Its life is conditioned by a whole range of perceptions which are unfamiliar to us: it may be conscious of the chemical constituents of its environment, be aware of the slightest disturbance, of the hydrostatic pressure and the quantity of dissolved oxygen which it breathes.

Its most developed sense would seem to be its taste. It is a mistake to call 'smell' that which can only be the exercise of taste. It is in fact unlikely that a sense of smell can operate in the water, for it is a sense which implies a transmission of scent by air. Fish taste water, they do not smell it; but can we speak with any assurance even of this? The importance of the olfactory lobes, the presence of nasal chambers, lead us on to assume the existence of an ill-defined sense which we must call a sense of smell. These organs are particularly well developed in sharks, who possess in addition an organ to indicate depth, a 'manometer' composed of cavities situated behind the snout.

The world of taste is infinitely richer for fish than for ourselves. We only taste things occasionally. They never stop. The taste-buds on the lips, the cheeks, the gills, and barbels gather in sensations of which we have no inkling. Our taste-buds are on the tongue alone and consequently operate only on what reaches them by way of the mouth, which presupposes a preliminary gesture and a deliberate attention. Light or sound strike eye or ear involuntarily, but to taste a thing we must open our mouth and place the object on the tongue. Fish, on the contrary, perceive these things immediately and without any conscious act of adaptation. They become aware of flavours at a very great distance, whether they are coming towards them or running away. This is why the line-fisherman uses bait and why the diver who goes in with a bit of meat strapped in his belt will find that fish flock towards him.

It would be possible to imagine a whole hierarchy of chemical elements according to a fish's likes and dislikes. They seek out some and avoid others, some are needed for their body and others will kill them. Their life depends on their aptitude for recognising such presences and this is, in truth, a unique sensibility, completely foreign to human beings, who grow aware of chemical substances only by having recourse to a complicated cross-reference system into which sight, smell and reasoning enter.

A fish's ear is quite unlike our own and has, except in the shark family, no communication with outside. It is a membranous bag enclosed in a bony cavity, one on each side and towards the back of the head. The actual organ of hearing, the cochlea, is of minute size. In addition to one, two or three semi-circular canals, chalky growths called otoliths are found, which reach considerable proportions in cod and bream, and by which a fish's age can be told.

The mechanism of these organs is worth describing: the chalky concretion is contained in a bladder full of liquid and covered on the inside by sensory hairs. When the animal moves the otolith rolls slowly from one hair to the next. Each of these tremors is transmitted to the brain and the fish is thus kept aware of the manner and amplitude of its three-dimensional displacement. If ichthyologists will allow me to risk the comparison, the otolith seems to me to be the fish's protection to enable it to avoid the 'blue ceiling', this trap where man lets himself be taken.

What can a fish hear? Research has led to contradictory conclusions. Some writers claim that fishes really hear and perceive only very slow vibrations, in particular the disturbance of the sea-bed. Line fishermen do not mind us talking beside them, but forbid us to walk about. All divers know that, on the other hand, water transmits sounds (much faster than the air, incidentally, at 4500 feet per second instead of 1000). If while diving we bang two bits of scrap-iron together, a jingling results which has no earthly resonance but which is a recognisable noise all the same. Under what form are fish aware of it? In company with a whole retinue of accessory sensations due to the tremor of the water? And is it not the vibration which for them is of the first importance? It is no easy distinction to make and one which is all the more difficult because in order to capture these waves fish make use of special organs, the so-called 'lateral line', whose importance seems much greater than that of the internal ear.

On this subject one piece of evidence is worth mentioning, that of Hans Hass, the Austrian diver who spent three months hunting in the Caribbean. Hans Hass and his companions have discovered that shouts under water make sharks run away. 'Sharks', he writes, 'went for us like cannon-balls and one of the three of us gave a cry of fear. None of us could remember afterwards who had cried out, but luckily it was a piercing shriek which went through the water with incredible results. At the last moment, as if stopped by some terrible blow, the three sharks wheeled away from us and bolted as fast as they had come. But one of the sharks, whose body was striated with clear stripes along its sides, seemed after the first moment to be ashamed of its fear, for when it was about a hundred feet away, it turned back and threw itself furiously at us to begin a new attack. But this time we all shrieked in a chorus which had the effect, literally, of turning it over on its side and, seized with panic, it fled, never to return.'

It's possible that the sound-waves of the human voice are painful to sharks. It is the only fish whose ear possesses outside communication and its sensitivity to vibration is enormous. Hans Hass had made another remark on this subject. We know that sharks arrive very quickly, sometimes from a long way off, as soon as a fish is wounded. The usual explanation is that they are attracted by the blood, though it is by no means easy to accept this for the quantity of blood is often infinitesimal and hardly has time to flow. And sharks turn up even if the fish has been caught on a hook and is not bleeding. According to Hans Hass the shark's attention is aroused by that particular beating of the fin which marks a fish's final flutter of life. The vibration transmitted through the water tells him of a death-agony in his territories. Such sensitivity is doubtless a product of his 'lateral line'.

This organ, found only in fishes and lacking in whales, consists of a series of tiny cavities and sensitive points running all along the body. Each of these perforations goes through the thickness of a scale and constitutes the opening of a tube which itself communicates with a longitudinal canal, followed by a nerve, the so-called 'lateral nerve'. To all these openings there are corresponding groups of microscopic cells furnished with cilia. The large size of the lateral nerve is a proof of the general importance of this system. In addition sensory crypts are disposed in great number on the creature's head, where they form a mosaic of smaller monitors.

All we can say of an organism so unlike our own senses is that it seems useful for capturing water vibrations. A fish's density, very close to that of its medium, makes it into a fine receiving set. The cilia of the organs along the lateral line vibrate to every wave and provide the possessor with signals to interpret. Picked up all along the body as they are, these sensations must scarcely ever cease. We may properly suppose that a fish lives in constant reception of a series of waves, each one of which has a meaning, and which requires a particular behaviour which it would be death to neglect. A fish whose eyes have been taken out will go on steering itself in the water and avoid obstacles or fly from danger, still being guided by its lateral line.

Opinions vary about fishes' sight. They used to be considered very short-sighted, and so they are—in the air. In the sea they have acute sight. But naturalists agree that a fish's eye, despite its complexity and even its apparent perfection, is very far from rendering the same services as do eyes for land-animals. We have explained how the horizon under water, even in the clear Mediterranean, is usually confined to a few yards; it is natural therefore that fishes make use of quite different organs than the eye to detect the approach of danger. Sight for them is simply an additional apparatus, which continues the indications that are more surely and more quickly provided by disturbances of the water or its chemical modifications. Professor Roule, for example, has proved that the range of vision of the Basilisk Blenny is only just over two feet. We can only repeat here what Rochon Duvigneaud has written:

> Creatures which know how to estimate the salinity and temperature of water and its pressure have plenty of ways of looking after themselves unknown to a visual animal like man.

Nevertheless with some aquatic animals the eye is capable of reaching a high degree of perfection: a fish from the Amazon which usually remains on the surface has eyes which are divided into two parts. The upper section enables it to see in the air, the lower to look under the surface.

On the other hand some fish from the greatest depths are totally blind. When the first drag-nets were let down several thousand feet and brought up these disabled creatures, ichthyologists came to the conclusion that they had lost the use of their eyes because they had become unnecessary in the darkness of the abyss. Since then they have revised their judgment, and now it is accepted that there are hardly any more blind creatures in the deep seas than on the surface. Neither is the darkness down there total, for many animals give out light. Some fish from great depths show eyes which are not atrophied but enormously developed, as if to take in the faintest glow. Such eyes are arranged like a telescope, projecting like two tubes with a prominent crystalline lens sometimes aimed upward (as in *Opisthoproctus soleatus* Vaillant fished up at 13,000 feet) and sometimes straight ahead (as in *Aceratias macrorhinus* found at 15,000).

Taste, hearing, sight are words which can only be roughly applied to the life of aquatic creatures. Everything must be transposed mentally. In the present state of our knowledge all that naturalists have been able to do is to study the anatomy of sense-organs in fishes and deduce the way they function. To go beyond, to describe the sensations connected with these organs, we should need to use observations and experiments which, though they may soon be available, are lacking at present. For there is every reason to hope that a diving ichthyologist, who gives his whole life to making observations under the surface, will bring us the evidence we need.

Even if we have read everything that naturalists have written about fishes' eyes and their bad sight, all their evidence does not prevail against the testimony of hunter and diver, both of whom well know that a thousand eyes are fixed upon them in the water. Now that we have dealt with their anatomy, I should like to mention the nature of a fish's gaze. The most beautiful is that of the *liche* (*Scymnus lichia*), a fish which has become too rare. Why does this creature bear the same name almost as the hind (*biche*) whose eyes so closely resemble its own? Melting eyes which seem to tremble with emotion and which give to this glossy bluish body, with a black stripe along it, the aura of an imaginary virginity. And then there are the round eyes, like those of a short-sighted pretty girl who won't wear glasses, which the grey mullet show when they swim to the surface to nibble the floating rubbish they adore. And the lively eyes of the sargues, as quick as the sharp flick of their tail which takes them out of reach at the very second when you seem to be getting to know them. And the golden eyes of the octopus with a line of shadow across them.

The dentex, as it promenades its brawny mass, casts a brief and furtive look at us like a prowling schoolmaster. There are also cruel stares which hold our eyes and make us hesitate; those of the moray and the conger: a cold insistent gaze which comes from little eyes like boot-buttons, icy in their coldness and which sway to the rhythm of the muscular neck, swollen round the nape like an all-in wrestler. Their physiognomy, quite different in every species, depends not only on the expression of the eye but on the shape of the head, the position and width of the eyes, the thickness of the lips, which gives to some the appearance of a sulky child, and, above all, the form of mouth and teeth.

Till recently ichthyology was, according to Professor Bertin, 'a science of carcasses'. The great *Natural History of Fishes*, by Cuvier and Valenciennes, which still retains its authority, was entirely written up from an examination of the collections of the Natural History Museum, which means from specimens preserved in alcohol.

Even though we watch them in the sea, we may no more come to understand fishes than we can understand what the world is like for a bee which distinguishes ultra-violet. We cannot imagine what its world looks like to a creature which lives in an unbroken current of imperceptible aquatic tremors.

Such a life of permanent sensation should be richer even than that of wild animals on land. What more can we say? To draw a distinction between reflex, instinct, and mind would not get us very far. And we must decide exactly the kind of fish we are discussing.

Thanks to the self-contained diving apparatus we can learn much more about the fish round our coasts. To divers who are tempted by this ambition M. Monod gives an excellent piece of advice. First get hold of a really good book on birds, for 'by learning exactly the kind of thing we know about birds we can tell precisely what we want to find out about fishes'.

After allowing fish an existence rich in experiences of taste, in chemical sensitivity and vibratory thrills, we must make quite sure they do not participate as well in social activities. It somewhat over-simplifies things to assume that the only relationship which exists is that between the eaters and the eaten. We have only to share in the underwater life of a Provençal creek by repeating our dives for a whole day or a whole season to become aware that the groupings of different species are not the result of blind chance nor even of biological laws alone, but the effect of certain affinities, perhaps even of particular sympathies and complicities which our grosser senses fail to recognise. I may be mistaken, but every time that I have dived and been able to surprise one of these groups in full gregarious action, I have felt I was intruding on a gathering of mutual relationships, a social function. Every time I have tried to get them to bear with me, remaining discreet and motionless, I have felt mysterious warnings circulating about my presence which were interpreted by the whole group. Generally my problem was how to reassure the most timid fishes present and so count on them to give the others more confidence. But it's no good cultivating the stupidest, like the breams, as our first friends, for in the scaly assemblies their opinion carries no weight. But if you can get your presence accepted by drum-fish then the sargues will calm down and finally the moment comes when you feel that you can do anything you like and no one will mind. Except kill.

In my attempt to draw a picture of these underwater encounters I have perhaps over-emphasised what takes place near the surface. Lower down, at a depths of 20 fathoms, an overwhelming tranquillity usually reigns. Such incidents as take place are over in a flash, and a powerful animal is gone in an instant. Here immobile creatures stand out in striking vividness, the bluish mauve of a starfish, the fretwork of *Retepora*, Neptune's lace, with its neon pallor, and the Prussian blue silhouette of *Gorgonia*. Nothing moves, nothing draws attention to itself, and in the depths of its caves the grouper, with its stiff bearing, lies motionless.

What is it like deeper still? What is life like, hour by hour and minute by minute, at 300 or 3000 feet? We have no idea. Those who have gone down to 300 or 350 feet with the self-contained diving apparatus have had enough to do to cope with their physiological difficulties, while the struggle against the deep-sea diver's delirium leaves scant room for scientific observation. But in the near future, thanks to new breathing equipment, we shall attain these depths and find out more secrets.

Even without going down so deep, we have, with means already at our disposal, many tasks left us. 'About the commonest and most ordinary creatures', writes M. René Legendre, Director of the Maritime Laboratory of the Collège de France at Concarneau, 'we are still in complete ignorance. In the case of many we have no idea how long they live, what they eat, how they reproduce themselves, what their chemical components are, their relationship with their medium, their reactions and their way of life.'

Despite the old analogy, Nature is not an open book which man reads easily. What it offers on a first examination is never as simple as it appears to be, especially when it deals with images of life; it is a gathering of separate but closely inter-woven existences, many of whose stake in life is the lowest.

Renan, who stifled a naturalist's vocation in his early days, clearly perceived that life is much too complicated to be reduced to simple terms. 'The French wish only to express ideas which are clear', he wrote in *The Future of Science*, 'but the most important laws, those which concern the transforma-tions of life, are not clear and we see them in a kind of twi-light.' Even so does the veiled lucidity of the sea-depths bathe the realities with which a diver comes in contact, and we need both sympathy and sensitivity to understand them. He must make the most of his luck, for he has immediate access to the heart of the sea world. Now the age of fishing blind, through which naturalists of the past tried to enlarge their knowledge scrap by scrap, is coming to an end. We must go back to school again, this time on the sea-bed.

# 4

# Caverns Under Water

*Life is not the way we see it. It is microscopic and all its characteristic*
*processes are on a scale measured in thousandths of a millimetre.*
ANDRE MAYER

THERE was a time when my friends and I used, somewhat
naïvely, to display our marine collections. Sometimes
there would be a shapeless sponge, sometimes one of
those mauvish-grey chalky petals, half-way between a potato
crisp and a rose-leaf. We were novices in diving and still more
so in marine biology. Every fragment we brought back from
the underwater world revealed afresh, when we got it home,
its infinite variety.

We set about sorting out and learning to recognise amongst
these organisms, sea-moss, sponges, ascidians, the tiny tubes of
annelids, and calcareous algae. Our scientific resources were
soon exhausted. However minute our trophy it displayed
biological riches exceeding all our powers of classification;
compound growths we did not know how to name, sometimes a soft brown creature half an inch long, or a rubbery
membrane. A solitary pebble from the sea presented insoluble
problems. The sea was throwing us what Paul Valéry calls
'the pieces left over after some night of high play', but it gave
no clue to the rules of the game.

We gathered enough pebbles to fill our pails and basins and
make the air stink all round. Yet the enchantment persisted:
between layers of limestone we came upon lacework, yellow
garlands, and pink embroidery.

Certain fragments dotted with what we took to be tiny
corals were merely Foraminifera, *Polytrema miniaceum*, and

what we had taken for stones turned out to be animal concretions.

We grew more and more skilful at solving these biological problems. It needed no great intelligence to realise that these accumulations repeated themselves with little variation. In some places they were mainly mauve, in others yellow: those which we thought *Botryllus* were really sponges.

Pascal as a child invented a new geometry by calling a circumference a circle and a straight line a stroke. We evolved, though less successfully, a zoology all our own with its private vocabulary. Thus we called calcareous algae (*Lithophyllum*) 'sea roses' after the desert rose of the Sahara. We were struggling to make some order out of chaos.

After cataloguing pebbles we grew more ambitious and went on to rocks. We no longer had to pick up 'pieces' left over from a game. On the ceilings of caves they were all set out ready for play. The trouble was we did not know how. We would stand gazing contemplatively at them, in turn puzzled and thoughtful, hoping for divine guidance, or at least some sort of key. When we emerged, unenlightened, *Gorgonia* bushes offered us less confusing pleasures.

At that time our favourite place was Cap Brun, near Toulon, in a cave whose three entrances all open a few yards from the surface. It is huge, fairly light in the middle, with only its base in shadow. The walls are completely hung with rich tapestry, not a square inch of rock bare, a creature-tapestry, all living flesh. Feeling your way round it, you touch alternate patches soft as velvet, resilient as rubber, hard as stone. A cellular mass, without fixed edges, creates a series of unique designs. Mosaic effects, areas of striking individual colour, startling reliefs, and floating tentacles like wall brackets show how every creature in this homogeneous mass retains its identity.

Enthusiastic neophytes, we hoped to be able to record these living pictures and work out their composition. But once out of the cave we seemed to lose our way: we were stretching both biology and our own knowledge beyond their limits.

Bewildered, we could scarcely recognise anything but the sea-anemones that blistered us or the sea-cucumbers which expelled their viscera in terror at our touch and left us with feelings of disgust and repulsion.

We began to collect caves as American millionaires collect twelfth-century shrines or Flemish tapestries. Their variety at every depth is one of the surprises of underwater life. There are dozens along the coast between Marseilles and Cannes, and soon I think we shall find them in hundreds. The cliffs over-hanging the shore are far less honeycombed. Why then so many caves below sea? Because on land every fissure is stopped up by rain-washed earth, while the sea fumbles away inces-santly to free every crevice below the surface. There may indeed be other reasons, which diver-geologists will discover.

These underwater caves, however, are not like those on land, and there are no long corridors with galleries opening out of them and connecting rooms. Speleologists might per-haps smile at marine grottos: especially if they think in terms of Padirac or Bramabiau. They are not the elaborate products of underground rivers. Some, perhaps, can be fairly compared, those for instance round the bases of Breton islands: at Groix or Belle-Ile, where local tradition has bolstered up reputations for some of them and excavations have revealed mysterious tunnels stretching away under layers of seaweed. There are opportunities here for divers with watertight lamps to practise their art.

Mediterranean caves are more exciting because light, often in extraordinary fashion, reaches into many of them: through courtyard windows, and skylights, sending shafts of sun to the sea-bed, through a sheet of oblique rays stretched like the canvas of a tent. Sometimes one has to dive through ink-dark depths before meeting the beam trained from a distant well-like opening. Then, without any of the contortions and acro-batics of a speleologist, the diver finds himself the centre of a firework display, with luminous fountains and silver bridges. But in good weather – and most sea-caves can only be entered in dead calm sea – all this liquid light is taut, frozen by rock and darkness.

Our knowledge of the underwater world is infinitesimal. The Mediterranean coast will have to be explored for generations before we get even a rough idea of it. But we already have a choice of caves, ranging from those at surface level, to some as much as 15 fathoms down.

The great 'Cathédrale Notre-Dame' of the Marine Alpine Club has its entrance above water and reaches a depth of 10 fathoms. Niolon, in the gulf of Marseilles, varies from 3 to 6 and the cave at Petit Mornas near Carry reaches 10 fathoms. The Cathédrale Notre-Dame has smooth walls, quite bare. So has the 'Grotte de Sainte-Marguerite' near Toulon. Their only beauty is in their light and shade. This exceptional lack of marine life is not due to their comparative darkness but to their shallowness and sandy, pebbled floor. A rough sea flings the pebbles up and wrenches off every living thing.

Our visits to these caves were invaluable. They were the beginning of a new education. I make no apology for the limitations of our landsmen's outlook, which were natural enough. Man has, for thousands of years, been conditioned by the reach of his hands and the level of his eyes. His outlook has not only been limited, but distorted. We must begin all over again. The attention we pay to animals, and the role we assign to them, depends almost entirely on our visual impressions. Even to-day we have to force ourselves to admit that bacteria play a more important part in our daily lives than do cows and sheep. The great performers below water are infinitely small. Foraminifera and radiolarians, consisting of a single cell and provided with a chalky or siliceous frame, have been able, as Michelet says, to 'pave the ocean'.

In the sea our human desire for logical explanation, a reason for everything, is often thwarted. When, in 1860, the German biologist, Haeckel, described and sketched several thousand kinds of radiolarians, this caused the greatest astonishment: in fact, studied under a microscope, these creatures have extremely complicated structures, shaped like tiaras or the lamps of mosques. Their latticed and siliceous skeleton is decorated with points and astragals perfect in symmetry. It is impossible to give a valid reason for this perfection. This complex and carefully constructed framework seems to have little importance for the life of the animal.

Amongst the more disconcerting forms of underwater life are the fixed animals, many of which look like plants or at least seaweeds. We must drop our preconceived ideas of animal and vegetable.

A diver who saw me handling *Gorgonia* remarked: 'It's odd how often one finds old pine branches down here!' I had great difficulty in convincing him that they were animals and not dead branches. In fact *Clematissa*, the great gorgonian found at depths of 60 feet or more off the Mediterranean coast, does remind one of a broken branch. It is, however, an animal, a species of Coelenterata. But it requires an effort to admit that a creature without head, limbs, or eyes, and hooked on to a rock, is an animal.

On land anything rooted is a plant, although there is an exception, a fungus that creeps on the surface of the ground. A carnivorous creature, motionless as *Gorgonia*, would die of hunger in our surface world, a herbivorous one would soon exhaust the fodder within its reach. Natural laws which we take for granted on land mean nothing in the sea, which itself nourishes and feeds stationary creatures and contains more roving plants than static ones: thus algae of the plankton, such as peridinians, are floating organisms. The human mind finds it hard to alter its convictions about things like that. Even the great Réaumur would not admit that there could be animal life in coral flowers.

*Clematissa*, the huge genus I have just mentioned, is not found in caves but on rock walls and in deep-sea labyrinths.

It is *Clematissa* which forms the network of branches spreading so thickly all over Le Vengeur. Its structure is not limestone, but a horny substance less fragile than one might expect. Crooked at its base, it sometimes reaches a height of 6 feet. In the water it is dark blue, nearly black. On the surface it looks rusty, leaving a sticky liquid on the fingers. There is another smaller, finer, and more elegant kind that lives in shallow water, sometimes at less than 15 feet. This is *Eunicella verrucosa*, salmon-pink in the sea but turning white a few days after being taken out of water. Its branches, often extremely intricate, are sometimes stretched taut, like straps; it depends on the state of the sea. Without being strictly a cave dweller, it likes crevices and narrow grooves, and runs horizontally or at slight angles along rock walls.

Animals like coral, sea-anemones or actinians reproduce themselves by shooting out fresh buds, for in the sea forms of reproduction normally associated with plants are at the disposal of animals: buds, cuttings, branches, as well as sexual reproduction. We still lack precise data about their rate of growth or life span. How long does it take for one of those prize creatures seized by divers to grow? Six months or six years? Is it a great disaster if a piece breaks off? Biologists still cannot say.

Probably conditions of growth vary according to surroundings, depth and abundance of weed. We know no more about the longevity of other marine creatures. All our data is based on observations made in aquariums, where conditions are entirely different. There the longevity of actinians, some of which have lived fifteen to twenty years in an aquarium, is astonishing. An *Actinia mesembryanthemum* put in the aquarium at Edinburgh in 1828 by Dallyell lived until 1887, dying at the age of sixty-eight.

It is time we began to gather precise details about essential problems: the sea itself must now be our aquarium. Professor Drach, carrying out diving experiments near the two laboratories he directs at Roscoff and at Nha Trang in Indo-China, marks certain creatures and weeds for special study. For *Gorgonia* and *Laminaria* he uses the willow rings with which chicken breeders mark their hatchings.

Patient and continuous observation alone can help us to break down our basic, often elementary, ignorance of the sea. Submarine photography will be invaluable, especially if it is consistently used, for it can provide us with the comparative information we desperately need.

How admirable it would be if one could write up one's underwater career on the scale and with the style of J. H. Fabre's *Entomological Reminiscences*. The history of marine life should, and must, be written in the sea. This is more than a mere phrase, however: when I dive, my equipment consists of a camera, a salad basket for specimens, a weighted drawing-board, a pencil, carefully sharpened so that the lead does not come away from the wood, a notebook. That's a heavy load, but worth while for the joy of being able to list at leisure the plants on rocks below the surface or the creatures clinging to the walls of caves.

Not perhaps the most daring of sporting exploits, for the best work is done at a depth of between 5 and 6 fathoms, sometimes in even shallower grottos. But I know no better intellectual exercise. When you have examined, and if possible identified, the various weeds and fish, you still have the job of describing them, noting their shape, colour, and position, before bringing in the specimen. Try it and you will realise how elusive the accurate, illuminating adjective can be, even with the time you get with self-contained diving gear and with the help of pencil and drawing-board. But, at least, with the subject before you, there is no temptation to cheat and try and get away with rough likenesses.

A man is quite alone, dead silence all round, and if he is a man of sensibility his only care will be to understand what he sees.

I am well aware that, apart from mussels and oysters as table foods, people are not interested in invertebrates. But a diver soon gets to know those motionless, or nearly motionless, species that are the occasional furniture of the ocean. Fish scatter at his approach, exacting more patience as objects of study, but sea-fans, polyps, sea-urchins, starfish, actinians and even octopus are willing victims of his curiosity. In spite of this, it is a formidable task, with the variety of species running into almost meaningless figures. There are 2500 kinds of sponge, 4500 Coelentera, including medusae and corals, 4000 echinoderms, including sea-urchins, starfish, Holothuria, or sea-cucumbers, 16,000 crustaceans, 60,000 molluscs and 30,000 recorded kinds of fish.

But getting to know these creatures at first-hand, under water, is a better introduction than books. A diver must go down to the sea-bed as others go out to fields and meadows. He must look at types and densities of sea creature, qualities of seaweed, the slope of rocks, light and shadow, at this liquid sky itself, as instinctively as a peasant watches clouds, soil, and dew. I long to bestow on the sea the same devotion as the peasant bears to the soil, his patient attention, his economy of movement. But a peasant of the sea must know its rhythms and seasons so well that he feels them in his blood.

In the Mediterranean spring at sea is in March. This spring does not, however, bring forth a thin surface layer of mould and vegetable: but 50 to 75 fathoms down the sleeping sea-bed stirs restlessly as the sun begins to train on it. A dense growth of vegetation, the unicellular algae called diatoms, of microscopic size, start devouring the nourishing salts. Thus the *phytoplankton* (Greek *phytos*, plant: and *planktos*, wandering) takes shape. These undersea prairies, with an annual production of 1400 tons to every square kilometre, are more fertile than any country meadow. Add to this, Radiolaria and Protozoa. Transparent beings, about the same density as water, these members of the plankton lap up nitrates and phosphates, so plentiful in the sea at the end of winter, and grow fat on them. But fish, who are mainly carnivorous, cannot assimilate vegetable matter. But a biological link, without which the life cycle of the sea would be broken, now comes to the rescue: larvae, not only fish larvae but the larvae of molluscs, crustaceans and echinoderms, gobble up this banquet of plants. And these herbivorous larvae of carnivorous creatures become, when gorged with algae, themselves prey to all flesh-eating creatures in the sea.

But even insatiable larval appetites cannot exhaust the plankton. Eventually these fortunate microscopic survivors reach a natural end: autumn breathes a last kiss on them and they slowly sink into the abyss. It is then that death's purpose becomes plain, for in the sea every process has a valuable biological function. A rain of dead bodies at last reaches the ocean floor. Plankton, herbivorous and carnivorous fish, make their final voyage to the great laboratories of the sea-bed. There they give back the water its phosphorus, nitrogen, and all those other elements life has borrowed from it.

Death in the sea is not like death on land. The slow fall of the dead bodies makes it impossible for them to reach their destination intact. During this slow descent to their underwater cemetery they begin to dissolve: the sea's continual friction wears away the hard parts, scales, shells, carapaces, bone. Stationary and roving creatures lie in ambush for these floating dead, waiting for their chance to make a meal of them. A squalid process, you might think. Perhaps, but we can't be sure.

Decay in the sea, like death in the sea, has its own laws, different from ours. Deep down, in the presence of salt and at a temperature of zero, matter does not decompose in the same way as up above. It turns into a ropy, jelly-like substance, in which marine bacteria flourish.

September sees this process reversed, phosphorus and nitrates brought back by currents to the surface. Thus in autumn the upper layers of the sea have their fertility renewed and so provide the necessary conditions for the new plankton that will develop in the spring.

If we are to found 'a peasantry of the sea' we must learn how to play upon this great marine cycle of life and death, discovering the most fertile places, the conditions best suited for reproduction, and making use of nature by following its laws. If you reflect on the long series of chances, the experiments and apprenticeships that led finally to our agricultural civilisation, you can see how far we have to go under water. We have hardly begun.

We are at the stage where, 10,000 years ago, our ancestors discovered that grain took root and ripened on the rubbish heaps at their doors. They discovered, too, that the wounded beasts they kept captive grew tame, even breeding in captivity. Thus agriculture and stockbreeding began. But what efforts, what constant demonstrations were needed to make man familiar with the coming of the seasons, the working of the soil, pruning, and the raising of cattle! We can begin to see the story, the religious imagery, the popularisation, that were necessary, starting centuries ago with Cretan vases and the Festivals of Athene, and ending at the portals of our cathedrals.

Now we are dreaming about doing the same in the sea, whose vast areas and variable climates hold out high hopes for another, miniature but brave and flourishing kind of life.

Maury, the biologist, has called the sea, 'a great nurse'. She presides like a gracious hostess over all her guests.

A cubic metre of sea water contains a third of a litre of living matter: that is, 8,000,000,000 Diatomaceae, 1300 fish eggs. These observations, taken on board the research ship *Valdivia*, during scientific tests in Fish Bay, near the Cape of Good Hope, mean that the 200 square kilometres of the Bay hold 160,600 million fish eggs and about 117 milliard larvae.

These figures, almost too vast to mean anything at all to us, give, at any rate, some idea of the sea's biological resources. But we need expert help to convert them into something of practical value. I was lucky, for I found a friend in Professor

J. M. Pérès, Director of the Maritime Station at Endoumes and through him I have learnt enough to see the possibilities in some sort of perspective.

Professor Pérès has, during exhaustive diving surveys of underwater caves in the Gulf of Marseilles, made lists and classifications whose evidence seems to me of great interest. He has found, amongst other things, many species usually met only in deep water. For example, *Axinella*, a kind of sponge normally fished at coral depth, more than 25 fathoms down, Sea-mosses, or Bryozoa, and Ascidia have confirmed that the caves and grottos shelter deep-sea creatures. Why is this so? It is still too soon to say, but Pérès has written:

> We know that the deeper we go down into the sea the weaker in proportion do the sun's rays become. On the other hand, they change qualitatively through the rapid absorption of infra-red. In caves and grottos it may be that only the quantitative change takes place and that as a result they attract specimens ordinarily found at much greater depths.

This seems to me an important conclusion. For the fact that sea creatures elect to live at shallow depths has some bearing on man's activities in the water. Quite what it is only the future can tell. But thanks also to Pérès, we know that this anomaly is associated with limestone rock. For instance, Niolon, Petit Mornas, En Vau, Le Brusc, etc. During a trip round Corsica, when diving surveys were made all round the coast, Pérès and his assistants were able to verify the important part that geological structure at great depths plays in the development of animal life.

Thus, bit by bit, we lay the foundations for our knowledge of the sea. We know already that life in salt water is not reproduced by accident. It is subject to overriding laws that destroy or multiply it. Only landsmen think the sea has uniformity; a wider range of landscapes is to be found there than above sea-level. It has great rocky canyons, rivered with mud or covered with seaweed, and it has deserts and jungles. There are areas as widely different as the Sahara from the Loire valley, the Beauce from the Alps. We know, too, that the chemical content of the water, its variations in density and temperature, condition its forms of life. The inhabitants of the ocean-bed require chemicals that only sea water provides. Almost all need calcium for scales, bones, or shells. Corals, molluscs and crustaceans need copper, and coral also uses fluorine, and silver. Oysters have to have zinc, gorgonians bromine, lobsters arsenic, prawns cobalt. . . .

But in addition to the main outlines of the biogeography of the sea, we also learn from small details. The position of an underwater cliff, its light, the shelter of a cave and the composition of its geological strata, offer us hints about the life we may expect to find there, just as on land the nature and situation of soil guide us in the planting of shrubs and crops.

M. Pierre Drach, a lecturer at the Sorbonne, underwent training with the *Groupe de Recherches sousmarines* at Toulon, to gain practical experience. He carried out forty deep dives in the Channel, the Mediterranean, and the South Atlantic. We owe him the first scientific surveys of life in deep and rocky coastal waters. But the importance of his work lies in the information he obtained on one of the most serious biological problems set us by the sea, if we are to make the best use of its riches: the question of living space. This is of special importance as far as stationary fauna are concerned.

Man has, by instinct, solved this problem for the only two species – oysters and mussels – he has so far cultivated. Let me retrace their instructive development.

# 5

# Breeding

*Some large, tame fish . . . helped us to get rid of the seaweed that
had stuck to our backs. . . . We saw wide-eyed admiration in their eyes
and we were pleased.*

JULES SUPERVIELLE
*L'Inconnue de la Seine*

FRENCHMEN have often said that their native soil and
peasant stock bequeath them certain qualities, a peculiar
wisdom, perhaps a way of thinking. Luckily that's not all.
The West is certainly imprisoned in its attachment to the land.
A leisureless civilisation has grown up to offset the easy-going
ways of the Mediterranean. The Western mind, close to the
soil, developed more sharpness than wisdom, a passion for
property, a taste for saving, a mistrust of strangers. These
rough qualities are easy to explain. Working on the land
itself creates the will to hold on to what has been so laboriously
won and the desire to hand it down.

But France is not all fields and meadows. The sea has
girdled her history from the prehistoric ports on the Atlantic
and the Channel to the harbours of Provence, from the coastal
trade of the Veneti to the bloodstained winterings of the
Norman rovers. But various historic factors have dissolved
such influences into our social history without leaving the im-
press so pronounced in Aegean civilisation, the basis of Chinese
tradition and Japanese economy. Along our coasts, to the edge
of Western Europe, the bond between man and the sea has
been relaxed for centuries. The youthful divers who explore
the caverns of Provence on holiday may be playing a more
important part than they seem. They are renewing the links
with our distant past. Soon they will coin the marine vocabu-

lary of which we stand in such need, and which we might have had if Caesar had not slaughtered all the Veneti, descendants of the men of the dolmens. We should have inherited their familiarity with seaweed and sea creatures. But Rome stamped out hellenism in Gaul and with it the Ligurians.

If divers have brought nothing from the sea to compare with Highland cattle or Buff Orpingtons, it is man's fault and not the sea's. Europe, unlike the Far East, has long ignored the sea, its creatures and its weed. Our outlook, moulded by peasant labour, has not grasped the idea of the sea as a source of nourishment. To us the soil is the great and only bountiful provider. Earth alone seems immutable with the enduring security of its plains and mountains, its vegetable covering, its soil where almost everything can be turned to use.

But a man must be very simple to think that the produce of the soil is a gift from God and that its fruits have been forthcoming from the outset. The one thing to which plough lands, woods and pastures bear witness is man's long, hard struggle. The landscape around us, all that we call nature, is the outcome of 8000 years' work still going on under our eyes. The Puys du Dome and Burgundy are the work of Neolithic man, but the Beauce was wooded in the time of the Merovingians.

Constant transformation of the soil has changed our landscape. Only the sea remains the same. The sea, untouched by man, has kept its caverns, its plateaux and valleys, its vegetation and its wild beasts. No one has interrupted the course of its life, or disturbed its plants. The only virgin world lies underneath the waves. The methods forced upon the land are only part of the work of the peasant in the West. He has not only left his lasting mark upon the soil, he has gone on developing new animals and plants. Originally there were no cereals in Europe. Everything that grows upon our soil to-day has come from distant places; first from Asia, much later from America. The corn of Neolithic man was Emmer wheat and even that, according to Vidal de la Blache, was a cul-

tivated plant and the centre of its distribution was Western
Asia. Wheat is the work of man. For man has not been satisfied merely with transporting plants, he has changed their
shape and form, enlarged their roots and leaves, and elaborated
their fruit and grain. He has transformed the animal world
by eliminating the most dangerous carnivorous creatures,
taming the ones he found most useful and developing the
qualities in them that he most appreciated.

To-day we see the results of this long task; but we do not
always grasp the price man paid. Viewed in perspective man
is the Creator, whether it be of cabbages, roses or sheep. It is
only the difficulty we have in tracing his methods that has
stopped us from doing him justice. It is impossible now to
discover the origin of maize. The same is true of dogs, the
first of all domestic animals. It is by no means certain that
there was ever a wild animal called a dog which man domesticated. On the other hand wolves, jackals and the Abyssinian
Caberu, an almost vanished creature, seem to have had some
part in its evolution. Domestic animals are all 'synthetic'.

But the sea never benefited from this immense amount of
work, that turned the earth into a food factory. Its plight was
comparable with that of the land in the old Stone Age. From
then till now, man's link with the Ocean has hardly changed.
A history of agriculture over that period would fill volumes,
man's efforts to exploit the Ocean could be written in a few
lines. His only achievements have been the breeding of oysters
and mussels, for out of 60,000 sorts of mollusc only two can be
said to have been 'domesticated' and that was only in historic
times several thousand years after the conquest of land animals.

Thanks to a few vase paintings we know for certain that
the Romans cultivated oysters in the time of Augustus.
According to Pliny, Sergius Aurata, grandfather of Catiline,
first had the idea of making oyster beds and fattening the
oyster. His work was done at Baia, in the Bay of Naples,
where oysters are still cultivated. The Romans also knew the

way to make an oyster 'disgorge', accustoming it by stages to close its gills when taken from the sea, so that it could be moved. Centuries went by before the West resumed that practice. The Chinese were certainly ahead of Sergius Aurata. Their ostreiculture has been going on for thousands of years and has continued on the spot until our own day. That is one more proof of the Far East's familiarity with the sea and the old marine forms of civilisation. Perhaps the Romans discovered nothing new; Chinese customs may have reached them through the Persians and the Greeks.

On the coasts of Gaul there were a number of oyster beds, both natural and artificial, copied from those in Italy whose products Ausonius has praised.

In 1759, Duhamel du Monceau counted about fifty oyster fisheries along the shore of the Channel and the Atlantic. It has often been said that the French forgot the secrets of ostreiculture between the Gallo-Roman period and the nineteenth century. That is not quite accurate. Our marine tradition has weakened, but it has not died out. M. Louis Lambert reminds us that for several centuries the oysters dragged up in the Bay of Mont-Saint-Michel were in beds off St Vaast-la-Hougue. At Etretat the oyster beds carved into the rock by the Marquis de Belvert in 1777 still exist.

It would be more accurate to say that this exploitation was inadequate to meet both the local demand for oysters and that of England, where most of them were exported. Intensive gathering of wild oysters for several centuries ended with the disappearance of the natural oyster beds. It is an interesting example of man's destructive work, despite the richness of marine life. But it also provides the first example under the pressure of necessity of a rational exploitation of the sea's wealth.

By 1853 eighteen out of twenty-eight beds in the Marennes region were completely exhausted and the rest were in danger of disappearing. Only three out of fifteen beds in the bay of St Brieuc were left. The same was roughly true at Granville and Cancale. The same dilemma was facing man in the sea as had confronted his prehistoric ancestors when they hunted down wild beasts till they were almost exterminated. In the nineteenth century the French had either to breed the oyster artificially or resign themselves to its extinction. But Coste, Professor of Embryology at the Collège de France and Inspector General of Fisheries, came to the rescue.

He dreamed of large-scale cultivation of the sea, of ambitious schemes for raising oysters, crustaceans and fish. For this purpose he founded the first laboratory of marine biology at Concarneau, which is still working as part of the Collège de France. But he only achieved one part of his ambition: oyster-breeding. After a visit to Italy, where he confirmed the persistence of Roman traditions and studied their application, Coste laid down the two model oyster beds at Cès and Crastorbe and put the domestication of oysters on a scientific basis. This was destined to make the fortune of most of our coastline. By 1871 there were 724 privately owned oyster beds in the Bay of Arcachon. In 1880 there were 4259 extending over 9884 acres and producing 195 million oysters. What seems natural to us to-day might then have been justly regarded as a miracle. Now the industry supports 300,000 people; 42,000 concessions, covering 19,768 acres, produce 60,000 tons of oysters a year.

The basic principle in breeding is to supply the larvae of wild oysters with havens to settle in. To collect these 'seed oysters' or 'spat' certain conditions of temperature and salinity are essential. The quantity and quality of the spat depend entirely on sea conditions. Oyster-breeders have for long tried to copy land techniques and to control the oyster's life from start to finish: regulating their fertility and larvae, feeding them like bird fanciers. Experiments are already being worked out in laboratories and will probably soon be put into practice.

One sort of oyster developed on our coasts, the Portuguese, does not really belong to the genus *Ostrea* but to the somewhat similar *Gryphaea*. Besides, its origin is not Portuguese but English. The Marquis de Pombal imported it from England about the year 1776 to populate the mouth of the Tagus. According to documents in the French Ministry of Marine the Portuguese oyster reached the coast of France in the following way: a steamship freighted by a certain Coycault received permission from the authorities to unload a cargo of oysters from the Tagus on the Crassat de Gralindes in the harbour at Arcachon. But bad weather drove him into the Gironde river and he sailed up it as far as Bordeaux. By then his cargo had begun to putrefy and infect the neighbourhood, so the local authorities intervened and asked the captain to put back to sea at once. He did not however wait to reach the sea before he got rid of his cargo. He had it all thrown into the river. But the oysters were not all dead. To that fact we owe the great deposit which stretches along the left bank of the Gironde as far as Byet-Saint-Christoly in the south, and Pointe de Grave in the north, and even as far out as the Ile d'Oléron and the Ile de Ré.

These rugged, prolific *portugaises* adapt themselves to the mud and to the other sea bottoms where the flat oyster cannot develop. Yet they have not, as was once feared, interfered with the culture of *Ostrea edulis*. The difference in their adaptability is probably due to the fact that the *portugaise* filters five or six times as much water through its gills as the flat oyster does in the same length of time.

For in the water the oyster stays open, and the gills which form four striated layers enable it to breathe, and maintain a current of water bringing the mollusc the microscopic organisms of the plankton on which it feeds. A mouth, a stomach, a liver, bowels and a heart, which can be seen beating when the oyster thins, are all the organs it possesses. Its senses are confined to one enveloping membrane: to this certain papilla are attached and these warn it of approaching danger so that it closes up its shell.

Note one essential difference: the *portugaise* has two distinct sexes, but the flat oyster is a hermaphrodite, or, more accurately, is by turns male and female. It changes its sex in one reproductive period and seldom fertilises its own eggs. Fertilisation takes place inside the shell of the flat oyster; *Gryphaea* lay their eggs in the water where they are immediately fructified by the male. One oyster can lay anything from a million to two million eggs, but breeders reckon that out of this enormous quantity only five or six reach maturity, i.e. live for the three or four years necessary for marketing.

Breeders do not only provide the larvae with somewhere to settle, varying from rocks, slate, old shells or, as at Arcachon, tiles. That is only a first encouraging step. Once they have made their home, man as usual goes on to defend them against their enemies. The oyster's deadliest enemies are crabs, molluscs that can pierce shells, some kinds of skate and, above all, starfish. These, like sea-urchins, belong to the phylum Echinodermata. But while a sea-urchin with its mass of prickles looks hostile and aggressive, starfish seem graceful and harmless. In fact they are voracious creatures, terrible devourers of flesh, though, unlike the sea-urchin, without teeth. To force a mollusc open a starfish clamps three of its rays on to one valve and two on to the other. The rays have powerful suckers, so there is a double pull, one in each direction, forcing the oyster shell apart. But having no means of mastication it distends its stomach over the tissues of the oyster when the opening is wide enough. Thanks to highly effective digestive juices the mollusc's flesh is soon assimilated. This done, the starfish retracts its stomach with five pairs of muscles.

'One starfish,' Louis Lambert wrote in his *Coquillages Comestibles*, 'can attack and overcome an oyster two-thirds its size; the average starfish can kill five yearling oysters every day for seven or eight months, only stopped by the cold and by the breeding period of June and July.'

The danger from the starfish is enhanced by its amazing

regenerative power. Whenever one of its rays is caught it
abandons it and the loss is not serious. It simply recreates it.
And the severed ray, once back in the sea, becomes another
starfish. You often find starfish, the product of mutilation,
with one large ray and four little ones. They bear the pleasing
name of 'comets'.

For a long time oyster-breeders knew nothing about these
powers of reproduction. When they found starfish in their
oyster beds, they just cut them up and threw them back into
the sea, thinking that they had destroyed them. Actually
they were increasing their number.

Oysters seem able to live a long time, at least twenty-five
or thirty years. The very large specimens with a 39-inch
shell, called 'horseshoes', are only old oysters. One caught
at Tahiti weighed 22 pounds. Finally a word about their
greenish colour. The Marennes have a great reputation for
their unique, green shade. It comes from a blue weed peculiar
to the Marennes district, and the oyster absorbs its pigmenta-
tion.

The food qualities of oysters have often been proclaimed:
they are richer in nitrates and minerals than milk, rather
poorer in fats, but with a content of copper, iron, zinc,
manganese, calcium and iodine. They contain vitamins A, D,
B1 and B2, C, E and PP.

Pearl-bearing oysters are not oysters proper but are a species
of *Margaritifera*. Unlike *Ostrea* or *Gryphaea* they have a foot
and cling on by a byssus (a filamentous tuft on the foot)
like mussels. The sexes are distinct, and at breeding-time the
females lay so many eggs that the water becomes a milky
colour. The male emits its sperm which fertilises the eggs in
the water. After two or three days the veliger larvae emerge
from the eggs and swim about before fixing themselves by
their byssus.

The secretion of a pearl is an act of defence on the part

of the mollusc, into whose body a parasite has thrust its way. This parasite is a sea worm, *Tetrarhyncus unionifactor*, whose complex life depends by turns on the lives of two other creatures, *Margaritifera* and the skate. This is the process: the larva of the worm inserts itself between the valves of a *Margaritifera*, pierces its mantle and stays there. In defence the mollusc tries to suffocate it under layers of calcium carbonate and after seven years it becomes a fair-sized pearl. Before the worm can reproduce, a skate, voracious for oysters, must eat the *Margaritifera*. As it devours it, the worm wriggles free and, attaching itself to the intestinal mucus of the skate, lays its eggs, which are liberated with the faeces of the skate and give rise to new larvae. These in their turn insert themselves into another pearl oyster, and the cycle begins all over again.

The cultivation of oysters went a step further with the success of pearl oyster-breeding at the beginning of the twentieth century. In this the Chinese were pioneers. For many centuries they knew the art of injecting into molluscs tin models on religious subjects which the creature covered gradually with mother of pearl. This was generally done to mussels, but the important thing is the process which led to the artificial culture of pearls. Later on the Japanese worked with a pearl oyster or more correctly *Margaritifera*.

They managed to place between the shell and the mantle a piece of mother of pearl, only the lower part of which was covered by the creature's secretion. So only half a pearl was produced and this had to be worked on. A breeder called Mikimoto, who was also a biologist, brought this technique to a high level of perfection by what was really a surgical grafting operation. The process was long kept secret. Each piece of mother of pearl is wrapped in a piece of *Margaritifera* flesh and grafted on to another *Margaritifera* without injuring it. In seven years a fine pearl is created in no way different from those found in 'wild' oysters. But during those seven years the growth of the *Margaritifera* must be assured, it must be protected from enemies and given the right food, temperature, and proper salinity. Equipment for the work has been set up in Japan, in the Bay of Ago. The molluscs are bred in real cages hanging from rafts and women divers care for them, watching their growth and classifying them on the sea-bed according to size.

The culture of the *Margaritifera* is perhaps the best example so far of what human ingenuity can do when applied to life in the seas around us.

There is a favourite story about mussels which is generally recognised as an indication of the exact date when breeding, under its learned name of Mytiliculture, first began.

In 1235 an Irish ship was wrecked in the Bay of L'Aiguillon off La Rochelle. The captain, Patrick Walton, took rooms ashore and started to trap wild duck with nets made fast to large stones in the mud. One day he noticed that the lower part of the stones was covered with mussel eggs, which later produced mussels much finer in quality than those on the rocks. Eventually increasing the number of his lines he set up the first mussel-breeding establishment on the Bay of L'Aiguillon, where the mussels are still highly prized for their excellence. He had realised that to develop marine life you must give it initial encouragement.

It is by no means certain that this story should be taken literally. Patrick Walton may not have been the inventor of this kind of sea-breeding. Breeding mussels seems to have gone on at Tarento in classic times and the tradition was not lost during the Middle Ages. We find references to mussel beds in twelfth-century manuscripts. It is quite likely that Patrick Walton knew all about Tarento and its mussel beds before he was wrecked in the Bay of L'Aiguillon.

Unlike the oyster, which fixes itself by a calcareous secretion from one of its valves, the mussel clings on by a bunch of filaments called a byssus. At the base of its foot are glands that secrete a viscous liquid which coagulates in water to form these filaments that enable it not only to cling to a fixed object but also to move in stages from place to place. First it stretches out its foot to where it wants to set up its new filaments, then emits a pasty, whitish liquid, spreading it in thin layers by continuous circular movements. 'This', wrote Boutan, 'acts like a piece of sealing-wax on an envelope.'

New filaments are thus created by which the mollusc moves itself. The process may be repetitive so mussels can find out the spots that suit them best, in particular those where they can feel the rise and fall of the sea. Their byssus is very strong and can stand up to a pull of 34 pounds weight.

A large number of motile cilia within the animal cause the passage of a continuous current of water by means of which it breathes and feeds. It can filter from 90 to 124 pints of water in twenty-four hours. What it absorbs through its mouth it can excrete in an hour and a quarter. But just what does it absorb? We cannot tell exactly, for we are still far from knowing the exact biology of even a shellfish as common as the mussel. M. Louis Lambert thinks that its food varies as much as does the plankton, and may consist of infusoria as well as diatoms and even certain larvae.

At breeding-time the organs of generation spread over practically the whole body. The eggs are red and the sperm white, so it is easy to distinguish the sexes. They are fertilised in the female, the current washing in the male spermatozoa. One mussel produces 500,000 larvae, already equipped with shell. After swimming about for a few days they fix themselves and grow quickly. Growth is determined by various factors; the light, the state of the sea and the temperature. Fresh water and mud fatten them, but rough seas develop the byssus and leave the mussel itself thin. Under favourable conditions they grow to one or two inches in nine or ten months.

The byssus of the common mussel, for all its strength, is not the finest that molluscs produce. The byssus of *Pinna nobilis* has been known since ancient times. Its threads, finer than silk, have been used all over the Mediterranean to spin fine stuffs for princes and prelates. Up till the eighteenth century the Italians made it into gloves and stockings. Jules Verne dresses the crew of the *Nautilus* in suits of it.

This great bivalve deserves a passing mention (although it has not been domesticated, which is perhaps a pity), because it is one of the great prizes for a modern diver. It is sometimes more than one and a half foot long. The shell is round at one end and sharply pointed at the other. Inside it is mother of pearl. Commandant le Prieur owns three fine specimens. It is said to be eatable. Professor Bertin says that the Neapolitans know the way to make it into a food. All they do is remove the pericardial pocket containing a black pigment with an acrid taste. Fishermen call it the 'pear'. Personally I have never eaten any at Naples, but when some of my friends tried the effect seemed to me disastrous. Doubtless because of the pear.

On the French coast feeble attempts have been made to breed other molluscs, winkles, cockles, and especially clams.

In America clams have been bred in favourable conditions more successfully than anywhere else. The clam is a burrowing mollusc, which buries itself in the sand and is protected by its hiding-place as well as its shell. But still having to breathe and absorb nourishment, it puts out two tubes of the same length from the rear end of its body. They are a kind of siphon. Motile cilia maintain a current of water, going in through one tube and coming out at the other, thus bringing them food and oxygen.

The latest thing to be bred under water is the sponge. In the Mediterranean you can find sponges at anything from 9 to 12 feet under the surface. They look like a blackish, yellow or pink mass, often seeming to be part of the underwater landscape. Some encrust the rocks in a layer the consistency of cardboard. There are white, speckled and chalk-coloured varieties, generously holed.

At a reasonable depth, say 15 to 20 fathoms, the diver can see them in their infinite variety. They branch out vertically, looking like chandeliers or wax candles. Some are shaped like funnels, others like tubes, cups or birds' nests, often varying greatly in shape and colour even within a single category. The immobility of a sponge long raised doubts about whether it was in fact an animal. Sponges are the most simple creatures made up of a collection of different-sized cells, the lowest form of Metazoa. They are little more than digestive bags, hardly differing from each other. When you buy a sponge it is only the skeleton of the creature, which, in toilet sponges at any rate, is chemically akin to silk. Alive, the sponge covers this skeleton, which may be limestone or horny flint, with flesh. Inside the central cavity numerous flagella constantly beat the water, bringing in fresh streams, enabling it to breathe and feed. The water flows in through the pores that riddle its skeleton and is exuded through a central orifice, the osculum.

There are male and female sponges. They reproduce in the central cavity and the eggs come out through the osculum. Sponges can also breed by budding and can regenerate after being mutilated. As the result of cell division they sometimes attain impressive dimensions. Sometimes two neighbouring sponges coalesce. In Europe the eggs form in spring and the larvae settle in summer. In the winter months the sponges seem to slow down their vital process, waking up again in the spring.

It is not hard to gather sponges by diving off the coast of Provence. These, though not equal in size or quality to those fished in Tunisia, are perfectly fit for domestic use. When they come out of the water they seem black and sticky. They must be washed and dried several times to eliminate all tissues likely to putrefy.

Sometimes there is a nauseating smell for several days. Before being sold, they are first washed in bromine, permanganate of potassium and hyposulphite of soda, then left to dry.

Commercial sponge fishing is practised in Tunisia, Syria,

off the Greek islands, the West Indies and the coast of Florida, usually at a depth of 60 to 120 feet. Each sort has its own names, velvet, lawn, coarse, etc., determined by quality. Fishermen in diving gear tend more and more to replace the naked plunger. Great care is taken to throw back into the sea fragments likely to grow again. A piece an inch wide takes roughly seven years to grow into a marketable commodity. Marine creatures often take longer to grow than people imagine, but their great fertility makes up for slowness.

Many attempts have been made to breed sponges artificially. The earliest was by Oscar Schmidt in 1862. The experiments made in the Adriatic, Tunisia and Florida have not so far yielded the results expected of them. In the Bahamas the Government has adopted methods which promise better things. There are three possible lines of approach: sponge breeding in earthenware tanks pierced with many holes, breeding from fragments, and settling larvae in 'collectors'. The last and most difficult method yields the quickest results. In two years it produces a sponge some 14 inches in diameter.

The laying of sponge beds on the oyster pattern requires complete knowledge of sponge biology, something we are still far from having. But the Bahamas experiments will add to our knowledge and help us in the Mediterranean. It is always wiser to breed than to pick, hunt or fish and it soon yields better results.

Several efforts have been made to domesticate crustaceans. Bumpus and Mead have been working on lobsters at Rhode Island in the USA. The method, described by D. K. Tressler (*Mar. Prod. of Com.*), is to confine the larvae of lobsters in fish wells that are either porous or pierced by many small holes, and then let down in the sea. In these fish wells a strong rotary and upward current is maintained by a mechanical process. Large females bearing eggs ready for hatching are put in boxes at the bottom of a tank on a pontoon. A propeller with wide blades is set in motion in the tank, and produces an upward current. Once the larva is hatched the current raises it up from the bottom of the tank just as in the natural process. Larvae one day old are put into a separate compartment which also has a propeller. This is very important as the larvae have a strong cannibal tendency. If larvae of different ages are mixed up the oldest devour the youngest, especially after the first moult. After the fourth moult the larvae are carried off in the fish wells by a gentle current. The time it takes to reach this stage depends on several factors, chiefly air-temperature and food.

Only half the eggs are lost in the process.

So far man has only known the sea as a great waste or a little fringe round the coast for children to paddle in. Now its half-opened depths offer possibilities worth dreaming about: the promise of co-operation between fish and men, the tokens of an understanding between them. I know of three attempts to tame the grouper by daily visits and gifts of fish. I took part in one. All three were unfruitful. That was not the fault of the grouper. All the same, it is no wild dream.

At Solutré, in Saône-et-Loire, there is a steep cliff at the foot of which thousands of horse skeletons have been found. They were all herded together by prehistoric huntsmen and driven over the edge. After that it was just a matter of cutting them in pieces and eating them. People of that time would certainly have been amazed had anyone told them there were better uses to be made of horses. But to-day, in just the same way, we drive tunny fish into nets and kill all the shad-fish at the mouths of our rivers. Nobody who has seen them with hooks in their flesh and the sea red with blood can seriously pretend that this is an operation worthy of us. I know there are times when we treat our fellow-men in the same way, but I never could follow such logic. That is a matter for men to settle among themselves. It is more the stupidity than the cruelty of nets that shocks me. It is a wholesale massacre smacking of primitive man.

The Romans used to tame morays. Some of these fish answered their masters' call and were adorned with gold rings passed through their gills. Some were mourned when they died and accorded funeral rites. The love of fish among the Romans was neither exceptional nor transitory. We have evidence of it for at least four centuries. Varronius refers to it in the second and Macrobius in the fifth century, quoting examples from their own experience.

Shall we ever get back to that? We have yet to establish a relationship between men and fish. It may be the work of the twentieth century.

Experiments in the big American aquaria and in marine biology stations, like Michel Lernet's on the isle of Bimini, show that fish, if not men, are quite ready to renew the old amity, for which they have as great an inclination as many mammals.

Americans have a greater taste than we have for these enormous establishments, in size and fittings more like zoos than modest aquaria. In enormous tanks Cetacea, even large sharks, sometimes live in conditions of semi-freedom.

The establishment at Key West in Florida is famous among ichthyologists for its tame fish. A Cuban keeper called Raoul has been getting amazing results. He will go to the edge of a great pond, clap his hands and whistle for his charges. Then he tells the visitors some of their names and calls at random for Joe, Juan, Molly or Dolores, who answer at once, coming to eat out of their master's hand. But Raoul can do better. He can call gently for a huge fish with a mottled skin, induce it to come nearer and finally to throw itself out of the water. Then it lies down on the edge, relaxing, while Raoul tickles and pats its sides and fins. At last, sliding his hand under the unresisting fish, he takes it up in his arms, gives it a piece of bread to swallow and puts it back in the water.

We all know that man has decimated the great sea mammals. We have had to control whale, seal and walrus fishing

4

because the animals became victims of wholesale massacre. But there are some sea beasts for which control can do little now. Two of them, the manatee and dugong, might certainly have become domestic animals. Zoologically they are classed on their own as Sirenia. In fact they are very like Cetacea and have a clear affinity to elephants. They have all that is needed for domestication. They are herbivorous mammals, their flesh has no taint of fish but is reminiscent of veal. Their oil and hides are very valuable. These inoffensive creatures have acclimatised themselves very well in zoological gardens. It would be easy to raise them under conditions of semi-freedom and it would save a species on the verge of extinction. Remember that the horse was about to disappear eight or ten thousand years ago when man began to domesticate it.

Our present stage of assisting the growth of fish, principally involving throwing back into the sea fish eggs that have been artificially fertilised, is almost over. We have reached the point of breeding fish in salt water. In captivity we have produced sole, turbot and mullet from the egg stage. Now a single female turbot produces 10,000,000 eggs. This shows that we can apply to the breeding of fish in salt water methods that have already been proved in fresh water. We know, thanks to artificial fertilisation, how to cross-breed successfully and how fish breeders have improved carp and trout, just as we have raised finer stocks of cattle and horses. Careful selection will retain the sea fish that offer us most: the greatest food value, the quickest growth and the best powers of reproduction. In breeding establishments along the coast fish will be reared at low cost.

# 6

## Courtship

*Being born is itself a great achievement.*
JEAN ROSTAND

OUR earliest encounters with octopuses, when we first went down with self-contained diving equipment, were picturesque. We had seen the beautiful photographs taken by J. Y. Cousteau, showing Frédéric Dumas playing in the sea with an octopus. We were convinced of the friendly character of these creatures and we resolved to show our sympathy at the first opportunity. Needless to say, we also hoped that some good photographs would result.

The meeting took place, but not quite as we hoped. To tell the truth the octopus seemed, from the outset, a shade too large. He was lurking near a wall of rock, quite low and in shadow, but he did not seem as agreeable and receptive as we had imagined. Each time we approached he swelled up, opening like an umbrella and assuming superb yellow tints. We took it that these were hostile. We watched in vain for some mark of sympathy or at any rate a gesture of tolerance. Finally, tired with waiting for a confidence that showed no signs of materialising, we went off to search for a colleague. The octopus took advantage of this to disappear, betraying a secret anxiety equal to our own, which, all things considered, was flattering. The photographs were useless. Luckily, with no proof to the contrary, we could say the octopus was especially large. Meeting an octopus of this size is something that only happens to beginners.

The specimens we subsequently met were of more reasonable dimensions, at least we considered them accessible and the meetings resulted in more or less friendly relationships. These first contacts remain painful, and there is a dramatic side to the tentative approaches between man and beast that I want to discuss, for some of them still cause me remorse.

Nothing, except the wrong kind of vanity, forces a diver to bait an octopus. The only time he may be forgiven is when through his own tact the contest he has provoked ends favourably. It does not always happen like this. The creature, when one sees it, is in a narrow crevice, its body in shadow, some tentacles outside, and the same colour as the rock and weed. The object is to make him come out, to lure him into open sea without annoying him. But the unfolding of the plot is impossible to predict. The animal can take fright, releasing its ink over the blue sky of the sea like a smoke-screen, and darkening it with invisible and rhythmic jets. Sometimes the tentacles wave, stretch, and the suckers grip the rock while the octopus hauls itself along, swaying uncertainly and then diving, like a man does, head thrust out, arms by the side, jerking itself into deep water. For a brief moment its yellow eyes gleam in mute supplication to the diver. That is the moment to stretch out a hand. At once a tentacle, neat and sharp as a whip, will grip it. The time has come for the man to show a kind of genius. Under the rough pressure of its suckers and the clammy touch of its stiff skin, he must not react in any kind of way or contract his fingers. The suckers, which are only muscles, will relax, the tentacles subside. You wear him across your hand like a scarf. And you are smeared with a powerful glue. The bewildered beast, drawn into open water and finding no support for its tentacles, can only hug this white, unfamiliar body. You are lucky if it cannot manage to reach a rock with one of its arms, for then you have to use the knife. But in any case the contest is over and the conclusion will be disagreeable. The diver has only to surface, holding this bundle of gripping, outraged flesh at arm's length, and throw it on the bottom of the boat or on the beach. Twined inside-out, the asphyxiated beast dies and the man, still out of breath, has to witness an agony he has not desired. It is a distasteful story.

My friend Robert Gruss does not have this kind of setback. He has a well-deserved reputation as an octopus-charmer. He is not only a first-class diver, but, still more rare, he is a man with a feeling for the deep and an intuitive understanding of its creatures. As a result he scarcely ever meets an obstinate octopus. What is more remarkable, he succeeds in stroking them, keeping them effortlessly twined around him and playing with them as though they were cats made of flannel. To him goes the honour of having shown that the octopus is an intelligent, domestic, and perhaps passionate animal.

The first inkling I had was when Gruss admitted to me that after long sessions the octopus dived down to the bottom, obviously exhausted.

It was in the aquarium at Monaco that my suspicions were confirmed. An octopus, a boarder at this aquarium, showed a familiarity at least the equal of Gruss's friends. With the permission of M. Belloc, the kindly assistant-director of the *Institut Océanographique*, I was able to witness the following scene: a keeper, chosen from among us, put his hand into the aquarium where the octopus seemed to be dreaming. The latter, as if recognising a friend's hand, stretched out a tentacle, then another, finally hauling up its whole body and offering it to caresses. But what the keeper's hand was softly stroking and handling, as Gruss had done, was not the head but the mantle. The mantle, however, contains, as well as the octopus's gills, its sexual organs. The keeper's and Gruss's caresses were exciting emotions of no uncertain kind.

The octopuses lavish similar caresses on one another during their own love-making. The male rubs his tentacles for a long time on the female's mantle and only obtains her consent through skilful tenacity. The movement in which he consummates his desire is not so simple: using one of his arms he has to empty into her palleal cavity the little horned sheaths containing the fertilising fluids: the spermatophores. Increasing his persuasive efforts he must introduce this arm into the palleal cavity of his mate. The two animals are then locked together. The arm of the male conveys the shudder of its orgasm the moment of consummation is reached. This curious way of mating takes time and sometimes the copulatory arm slightly suffocates the female by squeezing her gills, but from now on the male shows little anxiety for approval. During the mating, which lasts an hour or two, he holds the female by force and strikes her violently with his tentacles.

I don't know which appears odder to the uninitiated: the friendship which certain people have for snakes or that which others show for octopuses. The two feelings have in any case nothing in common and Gruss and I have no special liking for snakes. Far from it. And I think that many other divers who have no fear of octopuses have an obvious horror of snakes.

The octopus is a mollusc that crawls as much as it swims. But his way of crawling is not a snake's way: the tentacles with which he slowly explores the universe and tries out unknown flesh, such as a man, are as sensitive as any organic instrument and more accurate and effective than the human hand. We can only state their tactile value and their role in making love. Of course we cannot gauge their subtleties of erotic feeling. The mating of cuttle-fish is a long kiss, but while the animals are locked together mouth to mouth, their arms never stop caressing one another and intertwining.

There are other cephalopods with even stranger mating habits. For instance *Argonauta*, whose males and females rival one another in peculiarity. The male, who, like the octopus, uses a 'copulatory arm', discards it at the moment of consummation, leaving it in the female. He cannot perform again until a new arm has grown. *Nautilus*, in fact, does even better: he discards his arm before the embrace and this limb has to find its own way to the female organ, which sometimes receives it two or three times.

The female *Argonauta* has the more delicate habit of secreting a chalky nest where it lays its eggs. This white cradle, finely striped, is cupped in the crook of two of its arms. During the breeding period it goes about with its numerous family on this skiff, often wrongly called a shell. It is in fact a nest that only appears in motherhood.

Reproduction is the greatest achievement of marine life, more amazing and more ingenious than on land. The torpor to which cold and winter reduce the world of water, its growth and ripening, are only preparations for the reproductive act to which everything, even life itself, is sacrificed. Obsessed by it, marine animals squander themselves without apparent discretion and with an inventive generosity to which we may find ourselves too sensitive.

A human point of view makes us attach excessive importance to the preliminaries and outward signs of love-making, due no doubt to glandular causes and without effect on the continuity of the species.

There is probably no reason for the dazzling, highly coloured dress of the Mediterranean rainbow wrasse. All pairing, however fantastic or magical it may seem to us, ends in biological wedding and has no other object. All that contributes to it is only incidental—enchanting though it all may be. Let us allow the diver the right to switch from biology to sex and even to love. He may even live a passage from Lucretius: in water, Venus throws herself into desperate embraces that affect even the carapaces of crustaceans. Even in the smallest of them, love is consummated belly to belly or with the male astride his mate. Sometimes the pincer-shaped claws allow the male to lock the female in a cruel grip. The orgasm takes place while they are swimming and two males can fertilise one female at the same moment.

The male lobster, in the rutting season, paralyses the female and turns her over. Some of its claws work like pistons, enabling it to spread its sperm over the genital organs of its mate to await the arrival of the seed. Fertilisation takes place later and in the male's absence: the female again lies on her back, folding up her stomach so that her eggs can be reached by the sperm that she now carries. The eggs that have been fertilised stay fixed under the mother's body for the whole incubation period.

In crabs, the abdominal claws play the part of a speculum and facilitate the introduction of a double penis. Crustaceans, because of the shape of their shells, may have to take up difficult positions. Large sea-spiders, who have eloquent mating habits, combine their lyric performances with acrobatic feats: these alone enable these long-legged creatures to enjoy an embrace that their natural stiffness would seem to deny. And what can be said about the male crab capable of fertilising two females simultaneously while swimming, except that armour is no handicap to initiative. . . .

In spite of their appearance *Balanus*, *Pollicipes* and other barnacles that attach themselves to rocks or wharves, are not molluscs but crustaceans degenerated through sedentary life. Cuvier himself ranked them as molluscs. They are, however, shell-fish, sheltered under their carapaces, who wave tiny claws that maintain a nourishing current around them.

Their main interest is in the achievement of entertaining ways of reproduction. Each has an ovary and testicle, the latter being attached to its copulatory organ. The barnacle only fertilises itself as a last resort. Amongst them it is a service that neighbours render to each other. Held by their feet and sometimes quite far from the next one, barnacles stretch out to whoever is nearest a reproductive organ that is longer than their body, in the hope that a similar service will be rendered to them.

Too much talk about the reproduction of molluscs or minute crustaceans will end in us only remembering the small-scale side of marine love; the picturesque gestures, the hermaphroditism of ascidians are rites suitable for performance in aquariums or of interest to biologists. For the diver it is better to compare in their due season the erotic frenzies of ocean creatures. He is at complete liberty to study them in the sea.

I remember my amazement when I witnessed for the first time a scene whose meaning I did not immediately understand. It happened one morning in Magaud Cove, quite close in, at a spot where some rocks rose sharply to meet, a few yards below the surface, in a weed-covered and rather steep point. After diving I was swimming slowly back to the shore when I saw something gleaming amongst the weed on this rock: silvery reflections were weaving trails like skiers under water. I thought naïvely that a crate of fish, still in their pristine freshness, was spilling down the slope: but it was much better than that. Some good-sized fish were sliding down to the bottom, like children on the slopes of ramparts, and it was their bellies, shining and tensed, that filled the water with steel lights glinting like bayonets. But scarcely had they all reached the bottom than they were back, with a powerful stroke, to where they had started. And they began again. I thought the fish were playing. I glided lazily backwards and forwards over the carpet of seaweed before I guessed at the truth. I was watching the reproductive efforts of those fish that do not know the pleasures of mating.

Usually they lay their eggs in open sea. The female releases her eggs over which the male then spreads his sperm—the soft roe. But the creative power of the sea, its fertility, has nothing to equal it on land. It is quite true, however, that many dangers threaten the eggs and that therefore the perpetuation of the species requires an initial excess of spawn. The ling, a fish somewhat akin to a cod, lays from 25 to 30 million eggs. The size of the eggs varies, according to the species, from an inch or two to tenths of a millimetre, but these measurements bear no relation to the size of the animals which have laid them. The moon fish, which can measure 2 or 3 yards when fully grown, has half-millimetre eggs. Their size is more in inverse ratio to their abundance: those of skate are few but very large, while whiting's eggs, only a millimetre long, can be counted in tens of thousands. All these eggs vary in weight. The heaviest fall to the bottom or stick to seaweed or stationary animals; some because of their natural glue (as with herring's eggs), and others (like skate's eggs which are shaped like rectangular pouches held up at the corners by tendrils) due to their filaments. The lightest float, as for instance, mackerel, sardines, soles and cod, which at certain times of the year form a transparent and slightly sticky layer.

The incubation period varies in length according to the species and the temperature. It varies from 82 days at 5 degrees to 31 days at 10 degrees.

The eggs are sometimes the object of especial devotions, usually performed by the males. A few simply keep watch from the time of laying to hatching. Others, like the male sea-horse, have a brood pouch to which the female comes to lay. Jean Painlevé's beautiful film has shown to the outside world the remarkable erotic habits of sea-horses, with their curious protuberant stomachs, their prehensile tails. At the season of love, males and females meet in couples and slowly dance together a ballet full of contrition and formal greeting. At last they embrace; a union that takes place belly to belly, cheek to cheek, tails intertwined. In the male belly a pocket opens a little for the female belly to rest on. The eggs, sprinkled with sperm on the way, are thus passed from one to the other. The male has to carry his burden for two months, until the time comes for his confinement, which is more painful than one would suppose: by means of rubbing himself, twisting and twining about, he brings about a parturition of a kind, as his efforts clearly indicate, not at all common amongst males.

A number of fish, like gobies and wrasse, choose a nest for themselves: an empty shell, a crevice which they fit out and keep an eye on. The sea-stickleback does even better. The male gathers pieces of weed and sews them together on a thread from his urinary opening.

The sex of fish does not show itself till later. Hermaphroditism amongst them is often only an indecision of their youth. The animal keeps the attributes of both sexes until one dominates over the other. But there are also more determined hermaphrodites, such as sea-perch. Amongst giltheads, the same fish is successively male and female, while herrings, cod, and mackerel are also occasional hermaphrodites.

Sharks, however, have the most extraordinary courtships of all. These animals copulate. No one, except Lautréamont, can boast of having been present at the romantic rendezvous of one of the great, open-sea varieties. What Michelet once called 'the terrible and suspicious kiss of sharks' has only been possible to observe in an aquarium between the smaller kinds of shark like dog-fish, which can live and reproduce themselves in captivity. The eggs are fertilised inside the female. The male introduces his semen by means of an appendage called a clasper, which is a modified sort of pelvic fin.

In this embrace, which, as Michelet says, 'gives an idea of love between desperate lunatics', one can discern that the male coils himself tightly round the female so that the genital organs may come into contact.

Lampreys have for a long time been classified as fish. To-day they are ranked in a group apart because their internal structure is not that of vertebrates. Not only is the skeleton little more than a dorsal cord but their blood does not contain the haemoglobin proper to the blood of vertebrates. Moreover, the lamprey has no mouth; the circular opening that takes its place has no jawbone and is more like a sucker, in which horny lumps do the work of teeth and can, with the help of a rough tongue, tear up the victims with which it comes in contact. Such is the animal that, occupying a place apart in the animal kingdom, deserves it even more for the character of its love-making. This is both tragic and of a cruelty surpassing that of the praying mantis. It is, however, less well known.

Having spent several years in the sea and having reached a size of about a yard, the male lamprey returns to rivers and streams like salmon, sturgeon or shad. Its journey, which is begun in mid-winter, ends in the spring. When it reaches a clear stream, it fastens itself to a large stone with its sucker.

Its roes swollen, having undergone certain pre-nuptial physical modifications and having changed colour, it only leaves this stone to build up round it a kind of amphitheatre made of pebbles. It picks up the gravel from the river-bed with its sucker.

Attracted by the scent of the male, a female arrives in this carefully prepared nuptial chamber and glues her own sucker to the stone. The male then thrusts the horny edges of its mouth round the female's head. Thus an endless embrace begins that only death will sever. The two creatures, gripping one another but swayed by the current, make intense efforts to gratify their desire. The male, hugging the female, crushes her. He tries to penetrate her body with his genital organ, tearing open, bit by bit, the opening whence her eggs emerge. Almost gutted, she can do nothing to avoid a grasp that is wounding her to death. The male sucker gets more and more deeply embedded in her head, ripping her flesh, reaching into her eyes and finally her gills. But at last the laying is achieved: the female, completely disembowelled, no longer reacts to her husband's attacks. Immediately, he abandons her inert body, and as though she were only awaiting his desertion in order to die, she unloosens her sucker, lets herself be carried away by the current and goes off to end her agony in some hollow of the river-bed.

The male then resumes his sexual labours with other females, who, loitering about, are only waiting for him to finish. For him, too, these rites of love will end in death. After a final embrace the current will drag him away and his corpse will float past the watery graves of his victims.

The sexual life of certain fish is marked by long journeys undertaken at particular dates. These journeys differ according to the various kinds of fish. Salmon, sturgeon, shad, all at mating time find their way to fresh water streams and rivers. Eels, on the other hand, leave the rivers of Europe for the Sargasso Sea, off the coast of Florida. Naturalists have sought in vain for the reasons underlying these long journeys. Possibly they owe their origin to the dispositions of oceans and continents at some distant geological epoch. The eels which travel through the Channel are going up the over-run bed of the prehistoric Seine. The vicissitudes of eel migration were only finally cleared up in 1927, by a Danish scholar Dr Johannes Schmidt, who devoted his life to it and died at the task.

It was in 1904 that Schmidt was able to confirm that eels are born in the west Atlantic, south-east of the Bermudas, where the sea reaches a depth of more than 2500 fathoms. At first they are nothing more than transparent and colourless larvae, some 25 mm. long. They climb to the surface and allow themselves to drift towards the coasts of Europe. They are a year old when they reach the Azores, two years at Gibraltar, and three by the time they arrive on the French coast. They are now 7 or 8 cm. in length, pink and worm-shaped. These wandering larvae had already been observed and the 7 or 8 cm. specimens, known as glass-eels, had long been fished round the shores of Europe. But naturalists classified these animals as being of different species. Schmidt's achievement was to show that they were simply successive stages of the same fish: the eel.

These 'rough drafts' of eels, on reaching Europe, darken, turn green, and alter; they divide up into two groups. One lot goes to live in marshes and coastal lakes, the others work their way tirelessly up streams and rivers. These are the future females, who reach the interior while the future males remain near the coast. All European shores and river-banks, from Scandinavia to the Mediterranean, undergo this assault. The eels move from streams to rivers, fight their way through torrents and waterfalls, advance into damp grass and eventually find their way into lakes, ponds, ditches and even wells, miles from the sea. They live there five or eight years, undergoing a fresh transformation that ends in their sexual maturity. They then get ready to make the return journey and continue on until they reach the sea where the males are waiting. On the way they complete a further metamorphosis. Their bellies turn a silvery colour, their eyes widen, and their fins grow larger. Both males and females then travel together, along the ocean bed, the 4000 or so miles that separate them from the Sargasso Sea. During the whole of this voyage, made at a speed of 30 to 60 miles a day, the eels eat no food, have no rest, and, neglecting their natural functions, end by having the anus occluded. Finally, when they reach the mysterious Atlantic depths, they will lay, and the eggs will be fertilised. But the fate of these beasts come from so far to create new life still escapes us: probably the males and females die in the fulfilment of their wedding rites, for no eel has ever been caught after laying.

The love-affairs of whales are as interesting as those of the shark. In the rutting season they lavish spanking caresses on one another with their heavy fins and these embraces can be heard for miles around. They roll on top of one another and hug each other, but an actual mating has never been witnessed. On the lower part of a whale there are two openings, about two-thirds of the way down from the snout. The first is the genital orifice, the other the anus. One can tell the two sexes through the distance between these two orifices. In the female they are closer together.

Gestation lasts about a year and it appears that females only conceive every two years. The whale-calf probably measures at birth 7 or 8 yards. Foetuses already more than 5 yards long have been found in the wombs of pregnant whales. Suckling in water presents obvious difficulties. The mammary slits are in pairs on either side of the genital opening and they lead to small holes in which the teats are concealed. But how do the young calves suck their mother without stifling themselves under water? We now know how this *tour de force* is accomplished: the feeding in fact only lasts a very short time for the milk is so rich that even a small quantity has great nutritive value. Compared with 87 per cent water in cow's milk and

90 per cent in the milk of a mare, a whale's only contains 55 per cent. In addition the breast is surrounded by a muscle which enables the mother to compress it and under pressure shoot into her calf a jet of milk. She also lies on her side and raises a part of her body out of the water so that her infant can breathe.

About the habits, mating or feeding of deep-sea creatures we are still largely reduced to conjecture. The little that we know leads us to suppose that the way of life of these animals is hardly less surprising than their appearance. For example, Ceratioidea are the deep-sea fish most hampered with appendages. On their bodies, which seem too short, there are fibrous bushy growths. In *Ceratias holboelli* Kröy the specimens of a yard in length are females. Besides the usual excrescences, they carry parasitic animals fastened on their back, sides and head. These are the males whose size scarcely exceeds 8 cm. and of whom three or four may be present. These dwarfish and degenerate males, since they have neither digestive tube nor even a heart, are closely joined to the female's skin. The only organ which they have managed to keep is a huge testicle. Is this parasitism a device to ensure that there is no danger, in the eternal night of the deep sea, of the two sexes losing each other and the continuity of the species thereby suffering? To find out the answer we should have to witness the invisible, attain the inaccessible, and observe these creatures, not as corpses for dissection, but as animals that swim, eat and reproduce themselves.

# 7

# Virgin Seaweed

*Regardless of the sea, which they scarcely bother to look at, Norman peasants cut their corn on the very edge of cliffs, knowing nothing of the world that lies beyond.*

LUCIEN FEBVRE,
*The Earth and the Evolution of Man*

I COULD name the very day and hour when it first struck me that twentieth-century civilisation was lopsided. Just how lopsided it is will soon appear. Go 30 feet under water and you will find enough to see how clumsy and inadequate it is and how negligent in making use of the resources at its disposal under the sea.

A friend and I were walking under water among the rocky mazes of an inlet on the coast of Provence. It was summer. We had gone down into the sea through a gate of golden sunshine. The noon sun seemed to pierce the sea like a spike, reaching through dense blue water to sandy paths winding among rocks. We passed through a confused jumble of white rocks, sprouting violet sea-urchins, and then into the red and green light of rioting seaweed. Every rock face was covered with a different species: clear carpets of *Acetabularia*, little concave discs waving about on stems the colour of sprouting corn, the soft foam of *Cystoseira* as delightful to thrust one's fingers into as the fleece of chestnut-coloured poodles. Before us in the hazy light sargues pretended to be afraid, keeping their distance with gentle fin-flaps. Other blue, pink and dawn-gold fish idled in crystal caves. The soft, cool sea seemed designed for green plants and carefree life. But I knew that on the surface, a few hundred yards from the shore, there were gardens scorched by summer heat with not a blade of grass nor a single flower. Pale laurel trees shrivelled up in the sun, and the hillside was dotted with the yellow splodges of burnt shrubs. Leaves crumbled at a touch. In the market of Toulon a lettuce was a trophy.

In vain did the sea strew its glittering garlands; man had no use for them. The plants into which we thrust our hands were as useless a few feet under the sea as they would have been on Mars. This underwater garden, its riches sprawling untended, so near to man and yet so far from him, shocked us by the violence of its contrast.

Admittedly, it all looked more like china in colouring than food. We only glanced vaguely at these weeds on our way, but once more I found myself puzzled. Of the whole paraphernalia of the sea-bed, wrecks, creatures, water, rocks, and qualities of light, plants and weeds are the hardest to know. Slowly, and belatedly, I began to feel an interest in them.

We like flowers and trees, but who cares about seaweed? To a landsman it is as remote as the plants of the tropics. Its discovery is a matter of element, not continent. Sunk below the waves, swaying with the currents, trapped in the obscurity of the deep, before it stirs his interest a landsman must know more of it. Our liking for plants is bound up with their predictability. That goes for the suburban allotment holder as much as for the market gardener. It applies to the geranium in its pot on a balcony as much as to the garden of Versailles.

There are thousands of books, an oral tradition, to tell us how to plant, take cuttings, and reproduce our flowers. But how many people nowadays know that you can uproot seaweed and replant it, and tend sea vegetation as easily as an English lawn? We are supposed to learn at school how seaweed reproduces itself, but a great deal of academic learning perishes if we do not put it to a practical test.

I was once sufficiently inquisitive to open one of the little handbooks designed to tell schoolchildren all about animal and plant life. The chapter on seaweed begins like this. 'If you have ever been to the seaside you must have seen strands of seaweed, long brownish streamers like damp bits of rubber. Scientists call them algae.'

That sort of teaching is a distortion of fact. There is nothing in the following pages to rouse the curiosity of young children and everything calculated to make them indifferent.

It is easy to see why. Teachers cannot pass on an interest they do not feel. They use descriptive nouns and adjectives of unique tedium. They confine themselves to talking about brownish colours and rudimentary shapes, and anyone reading them would think all marine vegetation was the same, scant and drab. A prejudice put into your mind when you are ten years old is liable to distort your outlook all your life. Only someone who had never seen seaweed in the sea could think of it as being without beauty or subtlety.

It is quite true that beaches in Brittany reek with piles of long brownish streamers smothered in sand. In the grottos of Provence, at certain times of the year, there are heaps of shrivelled seaweed. This is the refuse of underwater gardens, thrown away and cast up by the waves. It is torn to shreds, has lost all its life and sometimes its very shape. Yet people think they can judge marine vegetation by this kind of rubbish.

It is as though one tried to study plant life ashore by examining a pile of dead leaves blown together by the autumn winds or to judge the beauty of a flower by picking one off a rubbish heap where the gardener has thrown it.

The study of seaweed is a science that has been unlucky. There are such sciences, which fall into the grip of a few good-natured cranks. Till the start of this century it was still a science confined to the coasts. People interested in seaweed would search the rocks at low tide.

The most daring would wade in to the waist, more often to the knees. Wuitner, when he refers to low tides says, 'It is at this not easily accessible level, where the collector of algae must not hesitate to wade in up to his knees, that he eventually reaps the reward of his efforts.'

The fact that we can smile nowadays at this tentative courage among men of learning shows what great changes have lately been wrought. Picking seaweed along the shore, even at the lowest tides, is like the work of a ragman rummaging in the rubbish, delighted to discover something intact. To-day the diver's equipment, even the simplest pair of underwater goggles, offers young botanists all the chances they could want. More fortunate than their predecessors, they can watch the living plant swaying with the waves, and in all the glory of its natural colouring. Luckier than the biologists themselves they can dive deep as they need, for nowadays self-contained diving gear enables a man to go down 130 or 150 feet, the greatest depth at which weed can flourish. But a few dives give little idea of plant life in the sea. As on land, it differs from place to place, from soil to soil, from one season to the next. Between a rocky and a sandy cove, from month to month, the plant life of the sea changes. This change can be divided into two stages; a rapid growth in the winter months and a period of reproduction in the autumn or the summer. How misleading and drab school textbooks make this imaginary sameness appear. To see the submarine landscape of the Mediterranean at its best you must visit it in the spring. Divers and collectors, scorning shallow water, often miss it in their search for deep-sea fish; they are in too much of a hurry to contemplate the landscape. Do not expect to find rich plant life in grottos; their 'vegetation' is entirely animal. Seaweeds never get so far, at most they cling to the entrance, where there is a patch of light. They flourish in favoured places, on rocky slopes looking to the south.

A naked diver can feel the variations of a marine landscape on his body. As he passes through tepid water to cold water and from a warm pool to a deep, cold ravine he travels from the world of *Cystoseira* to that of *Acetabularia*.

How hard it is to write about seaweed! Obviously the names of the various species convey nothing to a reader. It is one more case of scientific jargon deterring interest and providing a diver with nothing but monstrous compound Greek and Latin words. What can be done with *Porphyra umbilicalis* or *Chladophora rupestris*?

Beginners are still more confused when they find out that the classification of seaweed is uncertain. For a long time it was based on colour. For it transpired that colour was connected with other characteristics like shape and means of reproduction. But this was only a rough and ready classification, to which there are many exceptions. Thus this unscientific classification is not even convenient. And to reach it truth has had to be stretched, as algae do not always oblige the expert by taking on the colour they should. Most of them are provided with chlorophyll and only a thin brown, red or blue pigment conceals their basic green colour. Yet the old classification stands, qualified by several new sub-divisions varying according to the writer. The general tendency has been to separate the bacteria from the weed or at any rate to group together all microscopic algae under the name Schizophita.

I must now attempt some sort of description of the seaweed country travelled by fish and diver. Here, for instance, is how one of those little coves near Toulon, one that we have often explored, looks in spring.

The country round the cove is rockbound, with steep cliffs. Under water it stretches on through tumbled rocks, a maze of crags and corridors, dropping at some places anything from 12 to 15 feet in a sheer wall. The shore and sea-bed are both sand. The sea-bed is bare except for isolated tufts of plants with long leaves like uncut prairie grass. These are not seaweed but flowering plants: phanerogams, *Zostera*, and *Posidonia*, all dusty green. They bear tiny flowers in July and they fade in October. In the sea, waves play the part of winds ashore, not only blowing away the crumpled leaves but sweep-

ing off the little fluffy balls that you blunder on so unexpectedly in great profusion on the beaches of the south.

On rock walls that drop sheer down or slope with a smooth
surface, a carpet of small, pale-green discs spreads out waving
at the end of short stalks. In July they are a beautiful soft
green. At the end of September they turn white, then black.
These are *Acetabularia mediterranea*, of which we have spoken
already, the Latin word *Acetabulum* meaning cup. They are,
in fact, concave and become suckers when you put them on
the back of your hand.

Another sort, easy to pick out, are shaped like a rumpled
fan, nearly round, marbled with rose-coloured veins. They
grow in groups, and in flower are easy to photograph. Out of
the water they become quite flat and uninteresting. These are
Peacock Tails, *Padina pavonia*, but only in the Mediterranean
have I seen any that seemed to me beautiful. Elsewhere they
are dirty yellow and poor in quality.

Some rocks are covered by a thick carpet of brown weeds.
These are *Cystoseira*, already mentioned, soft to touch, with
slender crisp offshoots. They generally smother everything
near them, so you have to look further out in deeper water to
discover the more interesting sorts: the red and mauve
*Corallina* which divers compare with tufts of swan's down.

In muddier water, especially near Marseilles, the salad green
*Ulva* flourishes. *Enteromorpha clathrata* are as big as lettuces,
great sprouts, cottony in texture and puffed out like sponges.
Out of water they flatten out, becoming stringy and dishevelled like the hair of a drowned man.

I have gathered *Udotea* almost everywhere along the coast.
It is like a fern, delicately pleated at the edges, dark green and
with grey and pink splodges made by chalky deposits, with a
thin supple stem. At Cavalière I have found *Halimeda tuna*,
a chain of tiny spotted discs, seaweed formed like a small
fleshy plant.

Mediterranean seaweed is sparse and seems to be meticu-
lously scattered. Specialists call it 'poor'. At its thickest you

can hardly cover your hand in it. Grassland on shore is tall enough to conceal hares and field-mice. Mediterranean vegetation, apart from *Zostera*, like row on row of tufted leeks, does not even hide those large grey mottled starfish called *Asterias glacialis*.

Atlantic seaweed is much richer. When you have gathered armfuls of it, feeling the weight of its flesh in the sea, you get an inkling of the full lushness of marine vegetation. The species of *Laminaria* and *Fucus*, which run riot in the Atlantic, have the luxuriance of tropical growths. The moment you dive off the shores of Brittany you are conscious of the dense mass of seaweed, whether you just swim over it or thrust your way through the tangle. Its long blades and jagged offshoots with their little bladders are amazingly heavy. It is hard to realise that seaweed has no roots, no stalks and no leaves. While plants have different types of cell, a bark and absorbing hairs, seaweed has scarcely more than a single tissue poorly differentiated. This constitutes the 'holdfast' which is like a root but draws no nourishment from the soil. The same tissue forms what we call the stem, as well as the part which corresponds to leaves or blades.

The stem is cylindrical, it can be stiff or supple, and sometimes it constitutes a reserve of food. The vital part of the seaweed is at the junction of the stem and the foliage. When this is cut it dies.

Seaweed, instead of drawing nourishment from the soil like a plant, extracts it from the water around it. It is the blades, varying in their permeability at different seasons, which absorb nutritive substances and store them as reserves. In them some species fix iodine. Green or brown pigments make it possible to use solar radiation for the bio-chemical processes which govern their existence in the same way as with more highly developed green plants on land. By means of chlorophyll they can obtain carbon from carbon dioxide dissolved in the water and fix many chemicals. That is why no seaweed grows at a greater depth than the sun's rays can penetrate into the sea. But the depth varies according to climate. It is estimated at about 150 feet in the Atlantic and over 300 in the Mediterranean. But apparently this is only true of algae of a certain size, for vegetable cells of from three to five thousandth parts of a millimetre have been fished up in the Adriatic at a depth of 3600 feet.

Solar light, as I have said, is broken up as it passes through water and the different rays are swallowed up at various depths. The red rays are the first to disappear, close to the surface. Yet in land plants red rays are essential for photosynthesis. So there could be no vegetable life deeper than a few feet below the surface but for the fact that certain seaweeds secrete pigments which, at depths where the light intensity is low, enable assimilation to occur by means of light from the green instead of the red region of the spectrum.

It is just a hundred years since the mystery of the reproduction of seaweeds was solved. They used to be included among the lower plants or Cryptogams (Greek *cryptos*, hidden, and *gamos* marriage), and it was only in 1849 that the French naturalist Gustave Thuret discovered the reproductive organs that had so long escaped the notice of all observers. Five years later he revealed, in a conclusive essay, the mechanism of their fertilising power.

If you examine the various parts of the great Atlantic *Fucus* under a microscope you can make out two sorts of cavity: one shelters the bags holding the male elements, antherozoids, and the other the tiny balls which divide into the female oospheres. At maturity these cavities or male conceptacles emit drops of orange-coloured substance, which swell out with water, burst, and let out the antherozoids. These have filaments that enable them to move, and meet and fertilise the oospheres, freed from other conceptacles and in suspension in the sea. So an embryo is formed which drops down in the sea, develops and produces another specimen. In the sea where animals produce buds you would expect plants to lay eggs.

After all, it is very simple. The female red algae have filaments that can fish for the antherozoids, which are quite inert.
Other sorts have spores that form an additional reserve.

Botanists choose to say that algae are both the largest and
smallest plants. The heavy bundles of seaweed that swimmers
and divers bring up to wither on shore and be thrown aside
on the rocky headlands of Brittany are of very modest dimensions compared with Pacific or Antarctic vegetation. In those
waters there are giant *Macrocystis* over 50 yards long. In some
places these enormous weeds supported by their floats form
solid banks that entangle ships. *Lessonia fuscescens* has a cylindrical stem many feet high, the size of a tree trunk, from
which long branches grow. The whole thing looks like a tree-
fern.

It was probably the Sargasso Sea that first showed sailors
the importance of seaweed. Greeks and Phoenicians knew of
its existence, reckoning it as one of the greatest dangers of the
'Dark Sea'.

'On the 16th of September, 1492', Commandant Charcot
wrote in his *Christopher Columbus*, 'Columbus's caravels found
themselves about 900 miles from the Canaries, sailing through
masses of bright green seaweed. It looked to have been only
recently swept from shore, so they knew they must be near
some island. On the 19th Columbus took soundings thinking
that he was near the land from which the seaweed came, but
failed to touch the bottom at 200 fathoms.' It's not surprising
as he had sailed into the Sargasso Sea, where seaweed *floats*.
This huge sea prairie can grow above the greatest depths. It
stretches over 60,000 square miles of the surface in Mid-
Atlantic and moves with the wind. In summer it is blown
north by the south winds, in winter the north wind drives it
south-east. It was long, and quite wrongly, thought to be
made of seaweed swept away from the shores of America.
The name Sargasso, from the Spanish *sargazo* (seaweed),
really covers three kinds of fucoids, which can drift at large.

They have no holdfasts and no organs of reproduction. They can only increase by growing new branches. Their highly developed floats were mistaken for fruit by Christopher Columbus and his companions. Some navigators have stated that these plants can grow to a length of 500 yards. The true facts are less imposing. Sargasso weed probably reaches a length of 50 yards like *Macrocystis*, and seldom reaches one hundred.

Alongside these giants there are other weeds the size of a thousandth part of a millimetre. They vary a great deal in shape and make up a whole world of minute creatures whose variety and functions are still unknown.

*Navicula* alone has more than a thousand species, one of which, blue Navicula, gives Marennes oysters their greenish tint. Another microscopic weed, *Microcoleus cerbium*, is cultivated in salt marshes where it stops the formation of mud deposits. When we get to know more about this miniature world of weed and all its potentialities we shall probably find that it can be useful in many other ways. Peridinians and diatoms, whose size has to be reckoned in tenth parts of a millimetre, play an essential part in animal life in the sea. These marine plants, phytoplankton, are an essential link in the food chains of the oceans.

One day I and some friends had an experience in Brittany that taught us more about seaweed than all the textbooks. We took it into our heads to collect every species we could find in a little bay at Belle-Ile.

Of course we chose the largest specimens and we carried our catch ashore. We kept on slipping on the long glutinous streamers which crackled underfoot. I can still see that headland, with its sandy beach surrounded by blue rocks and our whole collection spread out to make a mermaid's catalogue. A strong smell of oysters and iodine rose from this tangle of rubber. Wuitner's handbook, splashed with water and full of sand, lay half-open at the mercy of our wet fingers.

We soon sorted out the *Laminaria*. They were all about 6 feet long, their holdfasts were intact and their fronds outspread. I can clearly see one of my friends slowly struggling through the foam draped in an enormous *Laminaria saccharina* with its ribbons trailing in the sea like a robe of state. Fishermen call it 'Neptune's cross-belt'. We examined the holdfasts of the strongest algae to find out their age. Every year a new ring grows on this bird of prey's claws. Four is the maximum.

*Laminaria cloustoni*, which is round and flat, was in perfect condition. But we found that some specimens showed one fan superimposed on the other and connected by a single, easily broken strip, for *Laminaria* is a flourishing plant which renews its foliage every year. The young frond grows at the top of the stem, pushing away last year's growth which does not fall off till the new frond has attained its full size. An amazing vegetable construction results, a pyramid of discs and blades superimposed on each other. They do not fall like leaves in the underwater winds, but drop off reluctantly through the movement of waves.

We had a fine specimen of *Saccorhiza bulbosa*, wavy, embossed, heavy and gilded. This is an annual. In one season it grows to considerable proportions. Professor Drach picked some 9 or 10 feet long. The wide festoons you see near the stem are called flounces. Botanical terms are seldom so happily chosen. One of us found a layer of *Chorda filum* 4 or 5 yards long and it smothered us in its green coils, rolled up like the curls on a wig. The Breton sea-beds are cluttered up in places by these coils, full of worm holes, that look rather like traps for divers but break off easily when you pull them.

*Fucus* has a circular, somewhat smaller holdfast than *Laminaria*. The stem is short and the foliage spreads out like a tree. Under the thallus a necklace of little balloons filled with air supports the heavy mass of seaweed. We got a little confused by all this, despite the help of our Wuitner, which got wetter and wetter as we fumbled it.

We set apart the red weeds, which were very fine and

transparent or stretched out like coral branches. They were harder to pluck. Hidden in the shelter of the brown sea-weeds, they were fragile and snapped off at the beat of the Atlantic waves. We had every shade of pink and red. The creamy pink of a Boucher nude came to life in the translucent flesh of *Nitophyllum* and *Delesseria sanguinea* displayed the pink rotundities of Renoir in his late period. *Plumularia* were like rose-coloured clouds in a flawless sunset. *Calliblepharis* was of a gooseberry shade that looked eatable. The carmine filaments of *Ceramium rubrum* when laid out on the sand looked like a blood-coloured design in anatomy. We could not help all these superb specimens having such names.

It was so late when we were finished that we could not, as we had promised ourselves, note all the agglomerations, parasitic growths and hybrids. In any case, I think that such a task was beyond us. Night was falling, switching on lighthouses in the distance. Our harvest piled up, smothered with sand, a shapeless mass in the darkness where the scurrying sandfleas leaped. In the half-light we rescued a few of the most portable specimens, sad at leaving the remainder to the indifference of passers-by. We alone had known these corpses in all their living sea beauty.

That was the sum total of our first efforts to gather plants in the Atlantic. You might well say that it was not much, but for the fact that it had shown divers accustomed to the poverty of Mediterranean sea-plants the luxuriance of Atlantic vegetation.

Yet the essential facts had escaped us and I only learnt them some time after, thanks to Professor Drach. The *Laminaria* zone does not go very deep, only to 45 or 60 feet. Absorbed in our plucking, restrained perhaps by the overwhelming impression of abundance unlike anything we knew on the coast of Provence, we did not dive very deep. A whole world had escaped us; we only touched its fringes. Professor Drach has explored it near Roscoff. The dense covering of seaweed is an 'undergrowth' (Professor Drach's word for it), concealing a plain rich in plants and animals. The stems of the larger sea-weeds vary between 2 feet 6 inches and 6 feet and shelter deep stretches of calm water where a whole marine life has made its home.

Deep below this garden of Eden where *Laminaria* ceases, you find a region inhabited by pink *Gorgonia*, creating for miles a landscape like that of the Mediterranean sea-bed.

Identifying the confusion of species and noting the various weeds that go to form the distinctive vegetation of a particular coast or bay is not, you may feel, very ambitious work. But no well-intentioned effort is useless in our present state of ignorance. The diver will certainly benefit from it. He will realise that this plant life, which he thought sprang up by hazard, is the result of special conditions of topography, light-ing, climate and the movement of water. He will see that just as every place has its own topography and vegetation so each has its distinctive animal life. Molluscs, polyps, crustaceans and fish seem to be connected with various rocks, sands and sea-weeds. The biological communities of plants and fish repeat a pattern which we can study. They form the basis of a new science, marine biogeography. Every description on which it is based constitutes the study of a particular facet, and all these facets put together give us the true picture of the sea.

There is no known poisonous or harmful seaweed. Some have an unpleasant taste, others like *Dyctopteris polypodioides* a disagreeable smell when they are fresh. Yet most of them have nothing that should put off an eventual consumer. Besides, for a long time and in all parts of the world efforts to make food from them have had varying degrees of success.

All coastal districts use or have used them with different measures of culinary skill. Making a quick survey of different regional recipes I must state clearly that they have been or are prepared in many other ways.

On the rocky coasts of North Carolina, Maine and New

England *Rhodymenia palmata* is eaten as a sweet. A giant sea-weed in California, *Necrocystis luekkeana*, is preserved in syrup. *Porphyra laciniata* (*anglice* laver) is boiled down and eaten with lemon juice. *Laurencia pinnatifida* is a Scottish condiment. *Alaria esculenta* is prepared as a cooked salad in Scotland, Ireland and Iceland. In various places they also eat *Iridea edulis*, *Chondrus crispus* and *mamillosus*, *Gelidium corneum*, *Laminaria digitata* and other species.

Lastly it is a well-known fact that they used to make bread from seaweed in Brittany, as well as a jelly, making great use of carragheen. Carragheen has unhappy associations because an ersatz table oil was made out of it during the last war.

All this shows that the consumption of seaweed in Europe or even America is not common. It is used as a condiment or to solidify other dishes. Professor Sauvageau, who has gone very carefully into the subject, has reached the conclusion that if at any time the poor in Scandinavia, the British Isles, the Faroes and Iceland ever ate certain seaweed, particularly *Alaria esculenta* and the young stems of *Laminaria flexicaulis*, they no longer do so.

It is quite different in the Far East. More than 70 sorts of seaweed are eaten to-day in the Hawaiian islands, China and Japan. They are seldom taken fresh, but are nearly always used in the making of products sold under names that vary according to the nature and quality of their preparation: Amanori, Funori, Tengusa, Asakuanori and so on. They generally look like thin square leaves nine inches or a foot long. They are mottled and brownish purple in colour, with a variety of tastes, and are used to make up all sorts of dishes, especially soups and sauces. Kombu is a mixture of seaweeds made up in a dozen ways and is an important food in Japan. But while Amanori and similar foods are made of red seaweed, Kombu derives from the brown *Laminaria*. D. K. Tressler distinguishes thirteen brands. The most common is the green, sliced variety. It is made by boiling the seaweed, then drying and compressing it. Later, it is sliced up, dried again, packed and delivered for sale. The chief centres of the industry are Osaka, Tokio and Hakodato. Cooked Kombu is eaten as a vegetable with meat or fish, in soups and sauces, with rice, in cakes or as a drink called Kombu tea.

There is every reason to believe that seaweed has been eaten since remote times. In fact, not only does it figure in the two oldest *cuisines*, Chinese and Japanese, but also among the dishes of many peoples in the Pacific islands.

All recipes for preparing Amanori and various brands of Kombu derive from ancient times. The methods used seem to go far back in local tradition. The same is true of seaweed cultivation, practised on a large scale in Japan.

At low tide bamboo stakes are driven into the ground to support bundles of faggots where the floating spores of weed come to rest. About January the seaweed plantations are at their best and yield their full crop. The harvest lasts till March. In April the breeding-grounds are cleared and prepared for next season's crop. In the last thirty years the Japanese have improved their seaweed cultivation by shifting to new ground with greater salt content and different aspect. The plants seem to have become more tender and often have an exquisite taste.

Despite intensive production and harvesting all round the coasts, Japan consumes more seaweed than it can produce and has to import large quantities from abroad.

Writers differ greatly about the nutritive qualities of sea-weed products. But they agree that it forms a valuable supplementary diet in the Far East where the staple food is rice and fish: fortunately the constipating qualities of seaweed are offset by the mucilage it contains.

Swallows' nests, a highly prized dish in the Far East, are made of a gelatinous substance which the birds form in their gizzards by swallowing, but not completely assimilating, certain red weeds found on the rocks at low tide. Millions of Chinese and Japanese flourish on a diet of seaweed, though any scientific study of it as food still bristles with difficulties.

We know more about it as cattle fodder, thanks to experiments made by Professor Sauvageau in 1918. During the food shortage in the Great War, Professor Sauvageau was called in to explore the possibilities of feeding animals on seaweed. Some horses were fed on it and nothing else. The seaweed was deprived of its mineral content, dried and gathered in September when it is at its most nourishing. Although the horses did the same work as before, they put on a great deal of weight, in one case 46 pounds, in another 40, in 15 days. The experiment proved that it takes 12 days to accustom animals to a seaweed diet. Perhaps a readjustment of the digestive organs would set up new bacteria. But as no such experiment has been made with man we do not know whether all human powers of digestion are the same or whether the nourishing qualities that the Japanese attribute to seaweed are not the result of long experience enabling them to digest it with ease.

In spite of the success achieved by Professor Sauvageau the use of seaweed as fodder has not become general and has not assumed industrial proportions. Yet there are some places where animals eat nothing else, particularly cows in Ile de Sein and in some parts of Ireland.

W. Besnard, an authority on marine foods, has written: 'We must look upon seaweed as a strengthening fodder which increases the weight of an animal.' A thorough experiment might lead to excellent results in raising horned cattle for meat or milking.

In agriculture seaweed is widely used. It helps to fertilise the land in Brittany, Ireland, Scotland and Japan, as well as in certain coastal districts of the United States. It is an excellent manure, absorbed by the soil more easily than common manures, as well as improving its quality. Roscoff owes its high fertility to seaweed; so does the Ile de Ré.

Sometimes it is used fresh, sometimes after fermenting for a whole year.

It is mixed with natural manure or superphosphates. As a fertiliser it has the advantage of suiting all types of soil, while being devoid of any kind of cryptogamic parasite or deleterious herb. It is, in chemical composition, something like farmyard manure but is richer in potassium salts. Its one disadvantage is its heaviness and awkwardness to handle.

One property of seaweed is its power to extract from sea water certain salts, which vary according to species. As much as 85 per cent of the weight of the thallus is made up of liquid whose salinity varies considerably. Some species readily absorb minerals. The Laminariales accumulate iodine and some of the red algae bromine also; *Padina pavonia* collects manganese. Potassium is more concentrated in all seaweeds than it is in the earth or the water. Iron, tin, titanium, sulphur, phosphorus, and silica, with traces of silver, copper, lead, antimony and arsenic, are also present. This property of seaweed has long been exploited for industrial purposes. The extraction of iodine and potassium from its ashes is a very old industry in France, unfortunately much smaller to-day.

In 1883 an Englishman called Stanford discovered algine, a substance peculiar to brown seaweeds. The metallic alginates, soluble or insoluble, alginates of copper, sodium, iron, potassium, ammonium and so forth, can be used in many ways nobody has yet experimented with. There are great possibilities.

In 1918, the Hercules Powder Company, near San Diego in California, used to treat 24,000 metric tons every month to extract acetone, potassium chlorate, ether, iodine and algine. But in spite of all these experiments, also more recent ones due to this last war, the exploitation of seaweed is still in its infancy.

A use for seaweed in industry has still to be found. It is quite impossible for the existing natural species to yield satisfactory results. No plant has ever presented man with riches enough to justify its intensive exploitation at the first attempt.

Selection, cultivation and cross-breeding may gradually diminish the large content of water and increase the residue of algine, iodine and other products. This is a matter for botanists. In 1855 Thuret began to cultivate seaweed artificially and produced the first cross-breeding achieved by man.

To-day we are far better equipped to apply the laws of genetics and exploit the profitable content of vegetable matter.

The example of the sugar beet is eloquent in this context. In its wild state beetroot is a coastal plant (*Beta maritima*) with a thin, woody root. In less than a century it has become a plant whose sugar content has more than trebled. In 1884 it was 5.5 per cent; to-day the Vilmorin beetroot yields 18 per cent. From an industrial point of view it is well to observe that the first sugar refinery in France, created by Napoleon, only dates from 1812, though the presence of sugar beetroot had been known since 1605. This one example shows that attempts to make use of plants on land have sometimes been slow, and have generally resulted in their complete transformation. The same will no doubt hold good for the produce of the sea.

# 8

## The Poetry of the Sea

*Une fraicheur, de la mer exhalée,*
*Me rend mon âme. . . . O puissance salée!*
*Courons à l'onde en rejaillir vivant!*
PAUL VALERY,
*Le Cimetière marin*

A LEADEN sky slowly seals up round me. I move with small strokes in this atmosphere, threatened by submarine night. I continue to go down, slipping over rays of sunlight half-strangled by shadow. A silky silence broken by the rhythm of my breathing: a comic gurgling, like pipe-bubbles, accompanies my exploration of this endless blue silk.

I roll over on my side for the pleasure of lying on a bed made of water. At the same time I bask in my loneliness: the sea-surface seems far away, no longer watered-silk but a dazzle of stars behind a sash of mist. Someone overhead is throwing pearls into the sea. No, I am wrong, these pearls are born of my breath. Rainbow-coloured bubbles climb at steep angles and break on the sky; there are fragments of gold everywhere. My own pattern of bubbles bears witness that I am still alive, that I have not foundered on the sea-bed.

But can I convince others that I am alive? Am I sure of it myself? With the help of two steel bottles filled with air an idea keeps going in the heart of the sea, but how hazardously!

'We commit his body to the deep.' The ritual phrase pronounced on board English ships when a corpse is thrown into the sea. I, too, am committed to the deep and similarly ballasted. Intoxication and dream cradle me. Reason still controls

me, but, enticed by every kind of treachery, it is poised for
mad flight to the sky, attracted by the slumbering phantoms
of the deep. I am the sleeper of the sea, the drowned but
conscious man drawn by the wires of dream into a dangerous
monologue.

Now comes the worst stage: the liquid sky over me is
blotted out and I know that it is no longer any use my looking
for it. I recognise this grisaille in which every colour is diluted:
I am in the body of the sea. . . . But the sea-bed cannot be
far off. I shall find land again, a false land rubbed away by
water, but firm, almost reassuring. Points of brilliance dance
in front of my eyes: fire-flies. Oppressive majesty of the
solitude in which I move, dazzled and blind. No more
familiar fish, or rocky labyrinths. I have never gone down so
far before. Perhaps I have over-estimated my resources and
agony is lying in wait amongst these shadows writhing below.
A sky of terrifying storm has taken possession of the sea. I
remember an evening when we were flying towards the
African coast and found it guarded by black columns. We
twisted between the pillars of tornados, into open corridors
like so many snares. The snare is here, in this crevice which I
am now going to explore.

Why do I think of Saint-Exupéry? Because of the storm,
the black sky, or because of the trap? The pilot of *Night Flight*
also discovered the trap in an opening between cyclones, and
he entered it as I am going to do, in spite of the distaste of that
uneasy I who keeps watch.

In my liquid sky I understand at last this fulfilment in
insecurity that was Saint-Exupéry's constant fulfilment. It was
studiously hidden from the eyes of landsmen and only showed
itself in his writing. He made it the excuse for his art. In public
he only built cardhouses with his strong and supple hands.

Land of Men. Sky of Men. Now, Sea of Men. Slow con-
quests. These metal constructions, which are called ships,
aeroplanes or diving suits, are worth less than the flesh which
inhabits them. Man alone is interesting: it is he who dares the

tempest, the cyclone in which Fabien perished, the abyss into which I am thrusting.

One must try and give a name to these confused reflections. But perhaps the human weight, the feeling of one's body that comes from submarine adventure and which machines take away, is the greatest sensation that the sea affords. Strange human weakness: a new world opens and man seeks an intercessor, the intervention of some enchanter to soothe the low reaches of his soul and persuade him to acts of daring. The low or the highest? That is a question for eternal debate. I am a lonely man who hesitates on the edge of the abyss and it is less with the abyss that I deliberate than with myself. Hans Hass tells how, in the Caribbean sea, at a moment of great pain, he recited Schiller's *Diver* to himself, over and over again. I am aware that the diver exploring the sea has recourse to almost every science: biology, optics, geology, chemistry, archaeology. But is poetry a driving force of oceanography? Perhaps. One day when I had asked Philippe Tailliez to describe to me how things looked at a depth of 30 to 45 fathoms he pondered a moment, looked at me and said with a doubtful expression:

'It's not possible. You can't describe it.'

Then he seemed to change his mind and his face brightened:

'Wait', he said, 'have you a Rimbaud?'

I went at once to get him the book.

Reading *Le Bateau ivre* under his breath, he marked some lines with his nail. They were:

> . . . *le poème*
> *De la mer infusé d'astres et lactescent* . . .

and

> *Baisers montant aux yeux des mers avec lenteur* . . .
> *Et l'éveil jaune et bleu des phosphores chanteurs.*

Each of these images, radiated by strange lights, enabled him to evoke a distant world. Only a few more words were needed to reach depths no one had ever described. Thus, poetic transcription was a stage towards knowledge of the abyss.

Describing the outside world, we in fact only describe ourselves and our interior feelings. Poetry is the medium through which we grope at expression. 'Poets', Freud said, 'are our masters in the exploration of the soul, for they are steeped in sources we have not yet made accessible to science.'

I imagine that, during the great prehistoric migrations from east to west, a people on the move one day stopped some distance from the sea. Leaving the bulk of the tribe there, an advance guard set out on reconnaissance and eventually reached this enormous expanse: a territory in which men drown, strange beasts reside and exotic sea-wrack floats. When they returned to the camp they appeared before the assembly of old chiefs and the eldest of them said:

'Speak!'

The members of the small advance party looked at one another in silence. At last one of them managed this simple expression:

'We have seen the great waste of water.'

Then he became silent. The elders got nothing more out of him.

One of the youngest members of the party next claimed attention: he was the son of the tribe's magician and already initiated into the mysteries of human life. He began by making something between a mutter and a chant: the noise of a still distant sea. The song rose, swelled and now it was the lowing of the sea, the quarrel of the ocean. The young man began to dance: he danced an imitation of the waves, one moment flowing and leisurely, the next violent, and he described the first man who had dived into them, battered and suffocated. He danced the fear and awe of everyone before this great unknown thing for which the tribe had not yet words. All those who had seen the sea corroborated him and the elders understood that a new element was entering the life of the tribe and that they would have to invent new magic rites and special prayers. Then much later it would be discussed as familiarly as forests, or the beasts of the earth or the thunder of the heavens.

I think it would be unwise to answer this theory by saying that we are no longer living in prehistoric times. The problems which the sea sets us are precisely those which the earth's surface set some 10,000 years ago. When the first divers tried to answer the questions of the tribe, they had no words at their disposal. They did not know what to say. And Philippe Tailliez had to enlist Rimbaud.

Why? Because poetry 'is steeped in sources we have not yet made accessible to science', because poetry, until scientific definitions can be realised, is the least misleading language in which to conjure up conditions that are barely recognisable and which the mind cannot grasp.

Because of this the poet is the precursor even of the expert in the exploration of the sea. Writers and poets are as important to its unravelling as biologists and geologists: they are intellectual weapons that strike at the heart of the mystery.

I often used to think of Colette on seaweed-picking expeditions. For fifteen years she spent the summer at Saint-Tropez. Was she aware that some few fathoms under water there were plants well worth her attention? Perhaps she alone would have been able to find the exact word for each of them, different words from the insipid adjectives of handbooks, words that now appear to us indispensable. She who discovered new tones in which to describe flowers, gardens, trees, dogs and cats, would have been the perfect translator of the underwater world. She would from the outset have imposed a certain distinction, she would have driven away staleness of phrasing, she would have been a safeguard.

She would have clarified for us these shadowy landscapes and revealed to us the secret reasons behind our preferences and dislikes in an element where we still lack positive enough reasons for liking or disliking. She would have put this luxuriant world on a human scale. Each piece of seaweed would have kept its consistency, each animal its beauty and energy. I cannot think without a sense of loss about the words with which she would have called up the seasons of the sea, each of which has its own colouring, its sparkle or sadness. While spring on land has been praised to destruction, the awakening of the ocean or the autumn of the waters has hardly been noticed, let alone described.

Only poetry can do justice to human experiment and ex-ploration. A writer has to snatch fragments of information from the unknown and make them coherent. How much would the East mean to us without Byron or Loti? What is true of the East is even more true of the sea-bed. When a biologist like Milne Edwards went down, as early as 1844, in a diving suit, we did not get much further. But if Loti, not content with having lived in Constantinople, had taken advantage of being a naval officer to do some diving, we might now have, as well as the description of the graveyard at Eyoub, some phrases, images or even a few words that would help in our intellectual exploration of the deep—an invaluable complement to physical exploration.

Bernardin de Saint-Pierre, in his *Etudes de la Nature*, wrote: 'The art of describing nature is so new that even the terms for it are not invented.' He was quite right, and he proved it by inventing them himself. It is to him that we are indebted for a great number of images of tropical vegetation, and even for the 'beaches stained with rose by coral dust . . .' He has handled with partial success 'the sky's vermilion', 'the ame-thyst of the sea', the 'saffron rays of the sun', the topaz and the emerald.

Rousseau had tried hard to play the part, but he was short-sighted and his style and landscapes have a certain shadowiness. Bernardin de Saint-Pierre had a painter's eye, he had travelled and he thought himself a naturalist. He possessed what the age needed: a vocabulary.

He did not in fact teach the French much about Nature or the colonies. Our ancestors had known the East since the Crusades, long before Lamartine and Loti. They knew of America before Chateaubriand, and even before Bernardin de Saint-Pierre they knew of the island now called Mauritius, but up till then known as Ile de France. But they spoke of them rarely and inconclusively, as we now speak of the ocean depths. A common language, with its search for style, its implied premises, the simplicity and subtlety that conversation requires, is only possible when there is some kind of literature to draw on.

Bernardin de Saint-Pierre is well aware of the debt his contemporaries owed him in 1786 for writing *Paul et Virginie*. The foreword to his novel begins like this:

> I have attempted, in this small work, something of a revolutionary nature. I have tried to depict a soil and vegetation different from those of Europe. Often enough our poets have left their lovers on the banks of streams, in meadows and in the shade of beech trees. I have wanted to bring them to the sea shore, to the edge of cliffs and into the shadow of coconuts, banana trees and flowering lemons.

An amateur naturalist, Bernardin de Saint-Pierre managed little more than nonsense. He corrupted his contemporaries with inaccurate facts about botany, anthropology, folk lore, corals and melons. But what did it matter? From a linguistic, social and historical point of view he did vital work: grapefruits, palmettos, macau-trees, guavas, became part of contemporary speech, were words used in society. Diderot, who knew much more about natural science, did not make use of half of them. He spoke the language of science, a specialist's vocabulary from which Bernardin de Saint-Pierre took just what he needed and did not worry too much about accuracy.

At the very least, one could say that the deep still awaits its

Bernardin de Saint-Pierre. It has at any rate failed to find anything better.

The underwater world's best stroke of luck was Paul Valéry. A fine swimmer, he spent his youth at Genoa and often used to bathe at Sète. He has described it in his journal:

> Three or four hours in warm water, deep between rocks: young men and young girls. We climbed on to rocks and dived into the sea all day long.

Perhaps he described the sea in a way no one had ever done before:

> I realise that I had a true passion for learning, but a craziness about the sea as well. My sole pastime, my only sport, was the purest of all: swimming. . . . It seems to me that I discover and recognise myself when I return to this universal element. I know nothing about harvests or about picking grapes. But to plunge into water, to move one's whole body, from head to toe, in its wild and graceful beauty; to twist about in its pure depths, this is for me a delight only comparable to love. . . . My body becomes the direct instrument of my mind, the author of its ideas.

For a long time I thought that *Le Cimetière marin* was only a soliloquy about the sea's surface, and that the poet had not splintered the mirror that fishing boats and yachts only scratch. . . . Either I read carelessly or I was not yet a perceptive diver. *Le Cimetière marin* reaches to the sea-bed, to this same deep that Valéry has called a 'roof'. It was this roof that concealed for so long the world that Valéry, the diver, had glimpsed. He is still the only one of our great writers to have described it in accurate language: 'When we think of the sea-bed, abandoning ourselves to its fantasy, we become poets of childlike wonder. We rove around like divers in coloured shadows laden with watered skies.'

There are some lines in *Charmes*, written about fresh water but which have often haunted me when sea-diving:

*Heureux vos corps fondus, Eaux planes et profondes!*
*Je suis seul! . . . Si les Dieux, les échos et les ondes*
*Et si tant de soupirs permettent qu'on le soit!*
*Seul! . . . mais encore celui qui s'approche de soi. . . .*

In fact I think I have read every work Valéry has written, in the hope of gathering some words or images that might be useful. The crop, unfortunately, is not great, but Valéry, I know, would not have blamed me for harvesting in his seafields. 'Poetry considered as an instrument of submarine exploration' – that would have been a subject to tempt him, and were he alive, he would have helped us.

I have, to tell the truth, been doing a little gleaning everywhere, or rather, to be more accurate, several of us are seeking together and without cease: we collect what we call 'submarine poetry'. I would not deny that there may be something naïve about our enthusiasm. Never mind, our reasons are practical and the method seems effective. For it is a question of acquiring a vocabulary, as one collects seaweed, and accustoming ourselves to life under water by getting hold of more reliable and more illuminating terms in which to define it. Naming is also discovering.

Such a poetry, to fulfil our needs, must not only be good in quality but must also have the right touch, and its images must inform. It should, too, be a light luggage to take with one underwater. Above all we are preparing poetic reserves, for use in winter or as consolation when we are far from the sea. Jules Supervielle has created some in two wonderful stories: *A Child of the High Seas* and *The Unknown Woman of the Seine.* The little girl to whom a sailor, dreaming with his elbows on the handrail, gave birth on the high seas, inhabits a watery village in mid-ocean. She moves with crystal limpidity and cannot die. Her father, the deckhand from Steenvoorde, 'had, one night, at a latitude of 55 degrees north and a longitude of 35 degrees west, thought of her for a long time and with terrible intensity, to the great unhappiness of that child'.

*The Unknown Woman of the Seine*, an insignificant piece of

miscellaneous news, writhed in the muddy waters of an estuary among a drowned society whose members were on intimate terms. Even her heart was muddy: like an underwater Bovary she died on the surface after having thrown into confusion the poetic world below in which she had refused to take off her clothes.

No worldly inconveniences mar these dreams between two seas. Supervielle must be congratulated on the great accuracy of his marine imagination. I don't know how he comes by it.

Lautréamont, somewhat surprisingly, has proved a disappointment. Perhaps because he was such a restless character. He was a man of surface waves more than of the tranquil deep. We can scarcely extract more from him than the apostrophe: 'Ancient Ocean, whose waves are crystal, I salute you. . . .' Perhaps it does not apply very well to the Mediterranean. On the other hand, for those who collect sea-plants and gorgonians, the following passage is encouraging. 'Ancient ocean, it is not impossible that you hide in your breast treasures for the future. Already you have given Man the whale. But you do not easily allow the greedy eyes of natural science to probe the thousand secrets of your most intimate anatomy: you are modest. Man boasts endlessly about trivialities. I salute you, ancient Ocean.'

As for the love-affairs of Maldoror and the female shark, they seem to lack the convincing details that might have been expected from so gratifying a relationship. Maldoror's metamorphosis into an octopus seemed to us to be slurred over: captious about his choice of adjectives we judged him as specialists.

I don't know which of us unearthed Moréas's invocation to Glaucus, our forerunner and the spiritual father of divers.

> *Couché dessus l'herbe marine,*
> *J'appellerai le sort de Glaque, le pêcheur.*

Moréas wrote, and we echo it till we are satiated. Our 'Moréas period' was short: if the poet loved the sea, he has only sung of its shores:

> *Je naquis au bord d'une mer dont la couleur passe*
> *En douceur le saphir oriental.  Des lys*
> *Y poussent dans le sable, ah, n'est-ce ta face*
> *Triste, les pâles lys de la mer natale.*

For one line that is both lively and beautiful, like

> *Téthys qui m'as vu naître, ô Méditerranée!*

an oppressively large mythology curbed our admiration:

> *Pour consoler mon cœur des trahisons,*
> *Je veux aimer, en de nobles chansons,*
> *Les doctes filles de Nérée:*
> *Glaucé, Cymothoé, Thoé,*
> *Protomédie et Panopeé,*
> *Eunice aux bras de rose, Eulimène, Hippothoé.*

Admittedly the name of Eunice reminded us of one of the gorgonians we were collecting: *Eunicella verrucosa*. But *Eunice* is also a sea worm. Moréas was rather a disappointment.

We had better luck with Apollinaire. He enriched our poetic capital with these lines from *Cortège*:

> *Les géants couverts d'algues passaient dans leur villes*
> *Sous-marines où les tours seules étaient des îles*
> *Et cette mer avec les clartés de ses profondeurs*
> *Coulait sang de mes veines et fait battre mon cœur.*

But above all we were enchanted by the last verse of *L'Emigrant de Landor Road*:

> *Gonfle-toi vers la nuit O Mer Les yeux des squales*
> *Jusqu'à l'aube ont guetté de loin avidement*
> *Des cadavres de jour rongés par les étoiles*
> *Parmi le bruit des flots et les derniers serments.*

A poem by Jacques Prévert immediately captivated us:

*Démons et Merveilles, vents et marées,*
*La Mer au loin déjà s'est retirée*
*Et toi, comme une algue doucement caressée par le vent,*
*Dans les sables du lit tu remues en rêvant.*

There is, too, the song from *Les Visiteurs du Soir*. It is useless to object to the coastal character of this poem, for the sea in its retreat has left the best part of itself. There are signs of genuine perception about the underwater world. Divers are not misled by it.

'Liquid skies' and 'coloured shadows' are accessible in future: submarine poetry, which was only a dream to Valéry, is a favour that the sea accords right away to a diver of sensibility. He only needs a minimum of gifts: a certain skill in the water, a quality of awe, curiosity. A submarine sensibility will one day become one of the attributes of the cultivated man, like taste or an ear for music.

However, this sensibility has still to find expression. It is a problem of language, a vital human problem only too rarely tackled. If Man is still a stranger in the sea, it is because he can neither give a name to what he sees there nor to his own sensations.

We have at our disposal a superbly rich vocabulary for the various techniques and incidents of country life. Here the words we use sometimes reach back beyond Indo-Europe to a neolithic language that has bequeathed to us the very name of the earth: TALA. But no fish name is Indo-European.

The Gauls christened the lark, the sheep, the horse, the plough and plough-share, but we are not indebted to them for a single term about ships or marine objects. Gallo-Roman, a labourers' language, did not create one word to do with the sea in ten centuries. French has existed on loans, on chance invasions and neighbourliness: *bateau* (boat) is of Saxon origin, *vague* (wave) comes from High German, *houle* (sea-swell) is Danish, *cingler* (to sail) Norse, *matelot* (sailor) is Picard, *dorade* (dolphin) comes from Provence, *hareng* (herring) from

Germany, *frégate* (frigate) is Italian, *amiral* (admiral) and *arsenal* Arabian. *Dock* and *paquebot* (packet-boat) were imported from England under Louis XIV and *yacht* was used in official correspondence for the first time by Colbert. *Canoë* (canoe) is a Caribbean word which came to us in an adapted form from the English. And so on.

This language, which, in describing activities on the sea's surface, has had to draw lavishly on other countries, is poorer still for dealing with life under water. If it is true, as M. Albert Dauzat has said, that 'a language at any period of its history constitutes an inventory of our knowledge', then our ignorance of oceanography is indeed considerable. Practically nothing under the sea has a French name. To talk about his discoveries a diver has to search vainly for words: none exist.

There are some, of course, in books. In biological textbooks, barbarous compounds derived from Greek and Latin attempt to describe the glittering creatures or pink and green plants whose beauty the diver can appreciate better than any scholar.

This huge body of words, without evocative power or poetic flair, was begotten in the nineteenth century. It was certainly needed. The vocabulary in general use at the time would never have been adequate to describe the 60,000 species of molluscs or the 16,000 crustaceans already identified. It was necessary to have recourse to an international language as well: a language whose Greek or Latin alternatives enabled sixteenth-century scholars to understand one another.

Because of this, all that science could offer divers by way of vocabulary consisted of harsh names, impossible to remember and sometimes to pronounce. Since modern languages only include common nouns for certain fish and a few molluscs, a day will come when the public will have to talk about copepods or describe seaweed by its names of *Calliblepharis* or *Rhodymenia*. It will not manage to avoid deforming the more difficult words, or inverting and making a travesty of them: it will drag them into life without scholars, linguists, and writers being able to do anything but applaud and finally

follow their example. But as we are still on the brink of this
submarine language, it is the right moment to interpose: this
is the time to invent common nouns.

It still depends on us to see that they are not too divorced
from their meaning. This creation of a language takes its place
in the slow formulation of a scientific vocabulary begun in
the nineteenth century and only assimilated capriciously into
common usage. For example, Pasteur's discoveries, to mention
only one case, have not been without linguistic consequences.
Infinitesimal particles, when they were discovered, had
no proper name. It was Doctor Sédillot, in a letter to the
Academy of Sciences in 1878, who invented the neologism
'microbe'. Linguists protested that microbe meant an animal
of short life, rather than a minute animal. And Littré was
called in twice to give his advice about the new word. He
confined himself to answering: 'Let the word take care of
itself, which it will do in any event.'

There is one word in submarine language that has triumph-
antly withstood, although altered in meaning, the test of time
as Littré prophesied. The word *scaphandrier* (diver). Invented
in 1769 by the Abbé de la Chapelle to describe an engine of
his invention, it was by no means a diving machine: but
consisting of a canvas waistcoat fitted with pieces of cork it
was designed to keep anyone who wore it above water. It
was, therefore, almost the opposite of a diving suit: a life-
belt. Boiste in 1800 was the first person to use the word in
the sense that ultimately prevailed. A Larousse of 1865 also
gives the form *scaphandreur*: it is evidently a word only half
vindicated. But its history is not finished. The same word is
used to-day when we mean an autonomous diver: there is no
other expression to distinguish a diver with a simple breathing apparatus from one with helmet and tube.

How annoying this gap is has been proved even in the
course of writing this book. The English have invented the
term 'frogman' and French papers have, in their turn, used

it to describe our diving friends of the URG. It is doubly inaccurate. In both cases equipment and performance are different: it has been explained that the closed circuit apparatus of the frogmen scarcely enabled them to go down beyond 4 fathoms while our divers, making use of compressed air, not oxygen, perform at 30 fathoms and deeper.

Besides, the term 'frogman' conjures up such a disagreeable attitude of the body, twisted and doubled up, while a diver's strokes, as I have tried to show, reveal the suppleness and grace of a flight into the 'liquid skies' so dear to Valéry. What writer, what poet will succeed in giving a name to the under-water traveller and rid us of frogs?

Photography is also a language. To-day it is the only universal language: it has established an authority that no other form of expression has ever known. Neither Egyptian bas-relief, nor Latin inscription, nor the stained-glass windows of cathedrals, nor even books, have had the suggestive power of the cinema. Submarine photography has had, from the very beginning, a poetic value. Films like those of Cousteau and Tailliez are not only faithful records of the marine world, but they contain images full of what one might call the residue of dreams. They can convey to an audience completely ignorant of sea life its whole range of poetic feeling. Whether we like it or not, the cinema will perhaps be the sole means of expressing this new sensibility.

What do we know of the poetic future except that poetry is rooted in Man's heart and that it can flourish under many forms? The cinematic vision of the sea-depths, more accurate still, thanks to colour photography, and soon to have stereo-scopic relief, will one day, perhaps, constitute the last fairyland allowed to those still able to dream.

There are already paintings done under water, though that does not mean they are good pictures. Perhaps it is still too soon to judge, and it might be wiser to wait till a good painter has attempted it, before deciding that the sea-bed does not lend itself to painting. In any case let us remember that it is not necessarily ambitious subjects that produce great works. A joint of beef, a roll of bread, an apple, were enough for Rembrandt, Manet, Cézanne, while the jungle has had scarcely any success except with the *douanier* Rousseau, who never saw it. What remains to be seen is whether the effect of certain themes on certain talents might not stir up new waves of artistic feeling, and whether the submarine world, revealed by a great painter, might not give birth to a school which would become a landmark in the history of art. Orientalism is an obvious comparison. Could submarine landscapes constitute a revelation analogous to that of the East under the brush of Delacroix? The answer is that one needs a Delacroix.

The painter's task in transcribing the underwater world is the same as the writer's or poet's. He, like them, has to convey sensations he cannot precisely express. He can only do it by a system of conventions, by suggestion and the invention of symbols.

Just as it will be some time before a submarine vocabulary, a dietetic seaweed, a domestic fish, will be at our disposal, so we cannot expect a good picture of the sea-depths at once.

Perhaps the world of water is more naturally accessible to the writer than to the artist. This shadowless light, spilling out in all directions, these congealed back drops, with their melancholy impressiveness, can be painted with words. Even the slight awareness excited in a diver's soul is enough for the task. On the other hand I am afraid that these blue waters shot with fish and filled with gorgonians will only have the interest of aquariums. Would a Corot installed before the subject, a Monet working on sea-anemones as though they were water-lilies, be able to snatch even some fragments of life from this dense, inhuman and sprawling wilderness?

There are underwater colours that are a writer's or painter's main problem. They are new and banal, explosive and

muffled; essentially unknown. By chance a friend of mine
went to see the windows of Chartres two days after having
dived 27 fathoms into the Mediterranean. The result was a
complicated argument that ended with us all standing in
front of the windows of the Sainte-Chapelle. In all sincerity
we had to admit that no window compared with the blue of
the Mediterranean depths.

The play of shapes in water, strange though it is, dis-
concerts us less. The human body, freed of its weight, assumes
an authority that it does not have on land. Sure of itself,
stable at last, light and soaring, it achieves in a moment
twenty almost perfect images. A certain human transparency,
both rippling and ethereal, dreamed of by da Vinci, the high-
flying figures of Tintoretto's *Paradise*, God, as portrayed by
Michelangelo, floating over Adam, come to life again at a
depth of 5 or 10 fathoms.

Finally, there is an activity of the mind that finds unexpected openings in the sea: philosophy. The enlightenment
that psychology can expect from diving has already been
mentioned. Metaphysics must also take its place there. I do
not think Man can restrain himself for long from taking with
him below water those preoccupations he has indulged in
other natural pursuits. A metaphysical animal on land, he
will be even more of one in the sea. I know divers who give
increased devotion to the marine world because they understand its part in the biological adventure of the planet. That
is a subject, however, that goes far beyond the framework of
this book. Let us only say enough to qualify the dreams of
philosopher-divers.

The extent to which the sea has played, and still plays, a
vital role in the phenomena of life, is no longer contested.
Our blood seems to preserve the traces of our marine past.
By means of an unknown device this blood is handed down
from person to person. Like the sea it transports its own salt
and gas: it is our interior sea.

These were the main theories of a French biologist, René Quinton. They created great excitement about 1900. To illustrate his theory Quinton showed how, in a dog, the blood could be replaced without causing death by sea water brought to the required temperature. In the body of a man weighing 11 stone, there are nearly 8 stone of salt water. Is it the balance of the past?

According to certain biologists, this sea-past is inscribed on our flesh before we see the light of day: the marks of our distant marine existence reappear on our bodies during the embryonic, or foetal stage. In the fourth week the human embryo produces, near the neck, branchial slits. It has aortic arches like a fish, and is endowed with a primitive kidney that disappears without having functioned. It is akin to the lamprey's kidney and is replaced by a kidney like a frog's which in its turn disappears. The foetus, at a certain stage of development, has only a notochord and a tubular heart with two cavities. Our children, our children's children, will re-create endlessly in their flesh these superseded fittings.

Even if, as Jean Rostand claims, man is grandson to the fish, we should still want to know how one of his ancestors passed from the world of water to that of air. This *tour de force* is not inconceivable: naturalists know of actual cases, even among vertebrates. This journey from marine life to life on land is generally considered a decisive victory, for only through it have we been able to reach the great estate called Man. But when the transition was made it did not symbolise immediate opportunity or greater liberty. The trials of life in the atmosphere are harder than conditions of existence under the sea surface. While a creature evolves in the water in three spatial dimensions and his body finds permanent support in a strong and nourishing environment, on land a man is half crushed, crippled by gravity.

Even to-day, after thousands of years in which to adapt ourselves to the land, we live a prey to all the ills that the disproportion between the specific weight of air and ourselves bring in its course. Our physical condition is very moderate. Only our intelligence, creating techniques, inventing instruments, makes up for our physical deficiencies. Also we are heirs to a rich tradition. The labours of the dead are the capital acquired by every human being on the day of his birth, but it is a bequest that does not enable the beneficiary to dispense with his wretched apprenticeship on earth. Walking, running, jumping, or even just standing, are for him neither spontaneous movements nor simple attitudes. Every child, on all fours, knows the truth of this. The human being is still too marine a creature to be completely at home on land, and too light to recapture the fish's unconcerned equilibrium in sea water.

With 6 pounds of lead tied to our belts we should be ready to return to our ancient haunts. Would it be a return to a lost paradise? This submarine awareness that we are developing, this unfamiliar balance should not be without their significance. The diver, enchanted by his discovery of a continent, fulfils the dreams of an ancestor remembering in him his marine happiness. Perhaps Man's tracks lead through the ocean in two directions.

# 9

# Museums Under the Sea

*There could have been no Rome without Ostia.*
HENRI PIRENNE

*Imperial Rome would have been as unthinkable without the granaries of Africa as Catholic Theology without the African St Augustin.*
MARC BLOCH

I REMEMBER that when the first art treasures were found in the Mediterranean, by means of self-contained diving apparatus, it struck me as highly inappropriate to describe such chance discoveries as marine archaeology. But we have progressed beyond that stage. And in the space of a few years marine archaeology has proved itself a science.

I want now to tell the story of the first treasures discovered under water. They display a wealth beyond the dreams of specialists. It is not so long ago since a sailor I knew would shrug his shoulders when I spoke to him of ancient wrecks.

'Don't talk to me about two-thousand-year-old wrecks,' he said. 'The sea battered them all to bits long ago.' He was wrong; and later he became a great devotee of marine archaeology.

In every age the sea has yielded ancient remains. Most of them have been hauled up near the shore. The fortunate finder was often the legendary poor fisherman whose catch contained a fragment of bronze or marble. Tales are told of persistent adventurers diving into the sea to retrieve a golden statue or lured on by some evil goddess. All this may have contributed to local folk-lore, but it seldom helped either the poor fishermen or the collections.

Generally, the help of divers had to be invoked to recover suspected treasure, so large-scale expeditions, seldom escaping the notice of authority, had to be organised.

Now all that has been changed. Self-contained diving gear has made it possible for a diver to explore the depths without the local authorities knowing much about it. Should he be lucky enough to discover a wreck, he can recover the less cumbersome fragments, bronzes, marble or bits of statuary without attracting official attention. To-day you can indulge in a secret treasure hunt right down to the sea-bed, with the added advantage that it is far harder to keep a watch on sunken treasure than it is to protect excavations on shore. So the modern despoiler is as great a pest to the serious archaeologist at sea as he is on land. In Egypt and Syria he has deprived us of invaluable data. He nearly always ransacks his objective to take away some portable trophy which he thinks valuable, he keeps his treasure house a secret, and we must blame him for the appearance of various objects impossible to date or catalogue.

But then all archaeology has been unfortunate in its early stages. There is no need to dwell on Lord Elgin, who tore the frieze off the Parthenon. The exploits of Hormuzd Rassam, who ransacked the Palace of Assurbanipal at night lest anyone should learn what he had found, are another example. Probably the most flagrant cases occur when prehistoric remains are explored. While scholars and journalists were arguing about some incomprehensible theory, with the newspapers having no monopoly in nonsense, less garrulous treasure seekers were blowing up the Breton Megaliths with explosives, hoping to find gold ornaments under them. Only the acuteness of an ordinary usher from the Town Hall saved the prehistoric monuments of Morbihan in Brittany, so that they could be properly examined and classified.

Submarine treasure hunts have caused, and still do cause, a great deal of harm. The first victims of this indiscriminate

looting were the galleys at Nemi in Italy. After being stripped
by various treasure seekers and inventors of diving gear, these
ships were broken up bit by bit during the fifteenth and six-
teenth centuries, in 1827 and, above all, in 1895. When they
were at last raised between 1927 and 1932 much of their
interest had been lost. The people who for centuries had been
stripping the ships of their bronze-work, statues, armament
and navigational gear only left the archaeologists the anchors,
admittedly of value, along with a few bronze rings. It must
be confessed that the ships fared no better above the water
than under it, for they were burnt during the Allied advance
in the last war.

Underwater looting went on till quite lately, as I shall
show. Three ancient wrecks have been retrieved, one at Cape
Artemision in Greece, north-east of Eubœa, one off Mahdia,
a little Tunisian port between Soussa and Sfax, and the third
at Albenga on the Italian Riviera. All have stories worth
telling.

Cape Artemision is full of classical associations. It juts out
into the sea where Aegean, Greek and Persian ships once
sailed. Within sight of the cape there was a three-day battle
between the Greek and Persian fleets in 480 B C. The Greeks
probably erected a monument to their victory on the shore.
At any rate in 1926 some fishermen caught a huge bronze
arm in their nets and showed it to antiquarians from Athens,
who clubbed together to organise an expedition, charter a
ship and enrol divers. They had just raised a huge statue of
Zeus six foot three inches high when the Greek police interfered and confiscated it (September 1928). Then the Government sent down divers. From a sunken ship where there
were still a number of rotting timbers, pebbles serving as
ballast and lead plates, they salvaged the forepart of a gallop-
ing horse and a young rider. These bronze lifesize figures are
now in the Museum at Athens. They suffered very little
damage under water and have now been completely restored.
'On what business was this ship engaged?' demanded Salomon

Reinach in the *Gazette des Beaux-Arts*. It was obviously carrying antique bronzes. But when was it loaded and when did it go down? Was it when the Romans were plundering Greece? Or when Christianity prevailed in the fourth century? Or during the Byzantine period? There is no clue. Nothing was salvaged, not even a coin, to tell us the date. The trouble lay in the way the work was carried out. You cannot turn a diver into an archaeologist in a few hours or make him understand to what he ought to pay attention or what he should reject 20 fathoms under the sea. All you can ask of him is to pick up the most easily visible things without taking any notice of rotting timbers. Shall we ever be able to persuade him that it is worth while exploring the mud, inch by inch, in the hope of finding a coin?

Admittedly one of the chief difficulties of marine archaeology is dating these nameless wrecks. Even when it carries a cargo of identifiable works of art there is no way to tell the name of the ship or the date when it went down. The Mahdia galley is another typical example. The story of its discovery is as follows: In June 1907 some sponge fishers off Mahdia between the Gulf of Hammamet and the Gulf of Gabes saw some objects looking like enormous guns covered with sand 20 fathoms under water. They must have appreciated the importance of their find, for shortly after Arab merchants in the Tunis bazaars were selling antiques ravaged by the sea. The Director of Antiquities in Tunis at the time was M. Alfred Merlin, later Director of the Louvre and a member of the Institute. Struck by this sudden appearance of ancient works of art he managed to find out their source. With the help of the Naval Officer in charge of Bizerta, Admiral Jean Baëhme, and an American patron, Mr James Hazen Hyde, six expeditions went down to the site off Mahdia between 1908 and 1913. The wreck was full of art treasures. Divers brought up a magnificent collection of statues, drinking vessels, candelabra and even a bronze bed.

They are now the pride of the Alaoui Museum at Tunis
where they fill five rooms.

For all the trouble M. Merlin took it was as hard for him
as for the men at Cape Artemision to regulate and supervise
the work done under water. A man who stays on the surface,
be he marine engineer or archaeologist, is in the hands of the
man who does the diving. He must believe what the diver
thinks he has seen and reckon with the ignorance, weariness
or the carelessness of one who is neither engineer nor archaeologist, but a simple manual labourer. But M. Merlin was sure
that after five expeditions the Mahdia wreck still had secrets
to disclose. Forty years later he fired the Undersea Research
Group of the French Navy with his keenness. Another expedition was fitted out to explore the site, this time equipped
with self-contained diving gear. It was worth trying anyway.
The fact that the wreck lay at a depth of 20 fathoms was in
itself a test for the new technique of underwater exploration.
It was questionable whether a naked diver could do useful
work at a depth which was considerable even for one fitted
with traditional diver's gear. Diving suits might well fit a man
to deal with stones and mud better than the simple equipment
of the French Navy.

The Undersea Research Group embarked on the despatch
boat *Elie Monnier*, taking the report drawn up by the sub-
lieutenant who had located the wreck in 1908. The place
should have been easy to find. Actually there was nothing on
the site but mud.

They had to make a preliminary survey of the bottom,
first with an underwater aquaplane, a sort of sledge towed by
a launch, whose depth could easily be regulated. But the sea
was rough and visibility limited to 18 or 20 feet. They went
for some miles along the sea-bed without seeing anything.
Then they fastened four buoys in position, linking them
together below the surface with cables. Other ropes were
made fast to these, marking off considerable stretches of the
sea-bed. In this way, foot by foot, they explored the sea over

an area of more than 7 acres. Again to no purpose. The search lasted five days. It was back-breaking work for the crew of seven divers. Swimming for long at great depths is extremely exhausting and the crew had gone down 20 fathoms 106 times in thirteen days.

As a last resort they made up their minds to enlarge the sphere of operations. The launch hitched to a cable a heavy weight to which a diver was clinging. The task was resumed. Commander Philippe Tailliez, the officer towed at the end of the cable, saw the 'big guns' at last. They had found the wreck. It lay 660 yards from the spot where it was charted. The 'big guns' were marble pillars. Only then was the work begun in earnest. The galley was not really a galley at all. It was a merchant-man, what we should now call a cargo boat. When it had been surveyed and measured by the URG the wreck proved to be 12 feet across and 40 long. It probably sank under the weight of its cargo. The URG could only measure the extent of the wreckage, which was probably greater than the original ship. The wreck lies in the sand 20 fathoms under water. It looks like a heap of marble columns still entangled in the remains of ribs, planks and keel. A few pieces of this 3000-year-old wood were examined and found to be covered with a protective varnish the formula of which is lost.

This heavy cargo, rummaged by divers in 1908, seemed hard to disentangle. To make a breach the divers of the URG first lifted four pillars, the heaviest weighing 3 metric tons. They were hauled up, not without damage, to the quarter-deck of the *Elie Monnier*. Two lead anchors, each weighing 700 kilograms, were also taken on board.

Unfortunately other duties awaited the *Elie Monnier*, and anyhow she had no dredger up to the work of dragging in such deep water. The divers improvised their methods, with fish swimming all round them. They groped around, flat on the liquid mud, for some new object to identify the wreck. Finally they gave up a hopeless task. The *Elie Monnier* weighed anchor after only eleven hours of effective work. So the Mahdia ship still keeps much of its mystery.

It seems to have cast five anchors, including the emergency anchor. They were all dropped in a line from the prow on the landward side. The ship must have gone down rapidly lengthways. Among the wreckage they found the bones of rabbits, sheep and pigs, as well as some human remains. Two of the five anchors were retrieved between 1908 and 1913 and are now in the Museum at Tunis. Two others recovered by the URG are in the Naval Museum at Toulon. None bears any inscription. They weigh between 600 and 700 kilograms. The emergency anchor, which is much heavier, must still be lying at the bottom of the sea. The ship seems to be in too bad a state for us to discover anything important about its original design. But that is no reason for thinking that further research would be futile. There must be many objects of interest buried in the mud or hidden under the pillars. True enough, the site has frequently been gone over. But in our present state of knowledge anything found on the spot might yield important clues to navigation in ancient times.

We must learn the right lessons from the examples of Artemision and Mahdia. In both cases it seems to me important that after 2000 years the divers still found the original timbers in place and the ships' lines pretty clear. Naturally both wrecks were so delicately balanced that the least touch upset them. But, however precarious their state, it would have been valuable for us if they had been more carefully handled. To read the accounts of the Artemision divers or of those who searched the Mahdia wreck between 1908 and 1913 is to regret that these relics handed down in their entirety were not in fact preserved. At Artemision there were still pieces of wood, leaden plaques and pebbles loaded as ballast. How was all this disposed of and by what means? It would have been of great importance to know and now we shall never do so. At Mahdia, despite the onslaught of the divers, Commander

Philippe Tailliez could still follow the lines of the ship, even though it had been dismembered. But forty years ago, while it was still intact, we might have learnt a great deal.

There was a similar case in Italy. The Institute of Ligurian Studies, whose admirable activities are well known, discovered that there was an ancient wreck 20 fathoms down opposite the little harbour of Albenga on the Italian Riviera. They induced Commandatore Quaglia to prospect. Quaglia is a Genoese shipowner who, thanks to diving apparatus designed for great depths, managed to retrieve the gold from the *Egypt* in 1921. He went to Albenga on his ship, the *Artiglio II*, and put his machines and men at the disposal of the archaeologists. Unfortunately his equipment was primarily devised to tear the armour plates off modern ships. It consisted of giant pincers, huge steel jaws worked by telephone instructions from a diver in an observation chamber. Their effect on a 2000-year-old wreck was often shattering. But the result was so satisfactory that it would be ungracious to denounce the means. 700 amphoras, the ship's entire plate, bits of helmets, and numerous bronze and lead objects were recovered. The presence of a melting pot, with lead still in it, would seem to show that the ships of antiquity could be repaired on the voyage. A large lead wheel, weighing about 200 pounds, with bits of rope on the spokes, is harder to account for. In its original setting it might have been easier to explain, but the steel jaws of the *Artiglio II* gripped it blindly and archaeologists are baffled.

I hope this case will be borne in mind when explorations are carried out on a wreck off the Côte d'Azur which promises ideal conditions. There a ship-load of amphoras sank, in the first century BC, off Anthéor in the roads at Agay. It lies 10 fathoms down. Shallow water and its proximity to the coast make it a relatively easy matter to explore. Too many divers have unfortunately already been at it, but though they may have taken away some amphoras the wreck has not been disturbed. Official operations are now about to start, and they may yield results as fruitful as the Albenga expedition, probably more profitable if the right methods are adopted. The Undersea Research Group have done some preliminary work clearing the site and have now reached the hull and brought up a few fragments. Only close collaboration between the Navy and the Ministry of Fine Arts, so infinitely desirable, can, however, enable us to clear the wreck completely and study it *in situ*.

Marine archaeology has now been revolutionised. There is no need, all the same, to blame a past that yielded the Marathon Boy, the Zeus from Artemision and the Youth from Anticythera, showpieces of our museums. But wreckage that the sea left untouched for 2000 years has, at one stroke of salvage, been irreparably damaged. We paid a high price for the recovery of those statues, and to go on in that way would be to make sacrifices out of all proportion for other works of art.

We now know what to do: in fact it is precisely the opposite to what, in our ignorance, we have always been doing. We must not go after a particular work of art, ignoring the general layout of the site itself and its details. Not only are these just as worth saving as the showpieces; everything about them is important. It is absurd to pretend that you cannot carry out marine archaeology with the same delicacy as on land. Several archaeologists have already done so. At Fos-sur-Mer, since 1948, the Société des Amis du vieil Istres has been examining a site 15 feet below the surface. The especial interest of their work lies in its being done with picks and all the essential archaeological equipment. Remains of a Roman house have been found and several artifacts, often as valuable artistically as historically, have been brought to light. Their value may be judged by the fact that they provide confirmation of the existence of a Roman settlement, dating from the time of Marius, on the site of a native village, a confirmation that archaeologists had not been able to obtain ashore.

In the small collection formed by divers at Istres there is a display of ancient pottery worthy of a great museum. Campanian vases, fine Arretine dishes, a small votive altar, which was discovered surrounded by its lamps, and some Roman provincial pottery are exhibits many archaeologists might envy.

I think their success is chiefly due to the fact that most of the explorers at Fos, and especially Dr Beaucaire who inspired their work, had learnt how to excavate by working on prehistoric sites ashore. So they used the same methods under water as they had already applied to the prehistoric remains round Istres. In the sea-bed they took note of the successive layers of earth. First there was a layer of sand, 15 inches thick, then one of fine mud dating from the time of the wreck. They went over it carefully, finding objects in perfect states of preservation. It is for reasons of this sort that trained archaeologists have made precious finds where ordinary divers could see nothing but mud.

Submarine archaeologists must in future work along the lines of the operations at Fos. There are, however, special difficulties, which I shall now try to clarify. Every wreck lies in the thick of animal and plant life. After several centuries it gets buried in mud, choked with seaweed and cluttered up with sea life, till it becomes impossible to make out what is or is not part of it. The blue-green underwater light blots out all shape and form, as at Anthéor, calcareous algae coat the pottery and date-mussels eat into the marble, as they did at Mahdia. The frontiers between wreck and marine vegetation are obliterated in the tangle of the sea-bed. You can wander for a long time in labyrinths of marine vegetation before finding out what is rock and what is a column overgrown with seaweed. It needs a skilled marine excavator to locate the most likely places and to sniff out valuable relics hiding under rioting sea-gardens.

When the area of exploration has been defined, a complete picture of the wreck and its surroundings must be built up. Every available means of underwater observation should be brought to bear. Photographs taken from every angle help in the reconstruction, especially if they can give some sort of picture of the ship's dimensions and general layout. I was lucky enough to follow work done under water by a marine draughtsman at Toulon. He began by drawing up an accurate and detailed plan of part of the harbour. I could not help thinking how valuable this preliminary but expert work would have been in the surveying of some ancient wreck for archaeological research.

It seems advisable to leave the actual wreck alone at first and start by clearing one side of the surrounding area. In this way every obstacle can be removed, and it will be possible to proceed, foot by foot, without risk of blocking the approaches to the wreck. In addition, there is, like this, less danger of missing something precious in the adjacent mud.

There are many difficulties, of which the sea is not the worst. It takes great effort of will to get a complete picture under water when vision is limited, shuttered by mud and seaweed. Under normal conditions it is rare to find anything you are not looking for. It is therefore as well to know what exactly there may be about.

No attempt worthy of the name has yet been made to explore an ancient wreck. Marine archaeology will only become a science by practice, patience and experience. But at any rate we now know enough to say that any excavation likely to fulfil its purpose will be heart-breakingly slow and will only be achieved under water. I do not think any undertaking of the sort can be directed from the surface. Given the potentialities of modern diving, it is still only by handling the various objects on the spot that a man can carry out his investigation, make up his mind where and when he is to proceed, as well as satisfy himself that he has exhausted every section before going on to the next. I cannot see how mere academic knowledge can save anybody from doing great harm under water; he must go down into the sea himself. On the other hand there is no reason why the great care and attention to minute detail required ashore should be dispensed with in the sea.

Marine excavation demands time, equipment and money. It also needs powerful dredgers and expert knowledge. How could it be otherwise? When you think of the scientific and financial resources harnessed to all the work done in Egypt and the Middle East, how could anyone expect marine excavation to be less costly? And is not a ship of the first century B C equally worth money and the latest equipment?

We already have good technical apparatus. Self-contained diving equipment makes it much easier than did the cumbersome old helmet and tube to bring things to the surface, to make drawings and take photographs. The Undersea Research Group has already shown what can be done by its accomplishments at Mahdia. It made an extremely instructive documentary film and its experiences provided useful lessons for the dredges so successfully used at Anthéor. But if we cannot have sufficient money for the best men and the latest excavatory devices, it would be better to have no more expeditions and leave the wrecks where they are for as long as possible. It has often been said that to excavate badly is worse than not to excavate at all. Both land and sea hold in their faithful keeping many things capable of eloquence. We must give them the means to speak.

Marine archaeology, I must make plain, is not just a branch of ordinary archaeology. It is a special science with its own rules and methods of research. Nor is the difference purely one of physical endurance. Land archaeologists, as we know, have made the most strenuous physical efforts: amongst others,

Renan, Paul Pelliot and Joseph Hackin. But the essential preliminary, and this is the point, for underwater research is
specialised psychological training. You cannot compare marine and land sites. The marine archaeologist must become, as
well as an expert diver, which is the easiest of his tasks, a
marine observer. This is a longer, much subtler process. Being
able to attach some meaning to the slightest clue about the
richness or extent of a site, is obviously more important under
water than on land. This kind of instinct only comes from
long practice, devotion and continual awareness. Every diver
knows what I mean.

'Every year our underwater senses improve', Henri Broussard, one of the best and most highly trained divers I know,
once said to me. On its last expedition the Club Alpin discovered valuable archaeological remains under water in places
that had been surveyed many times previously without
result.

We are getting accustomed to using our eyes under water
and our archaeological sense is developing. But this is only a
fraction of what is needed. If it is true to say that geology,
geography, ability to read inscriptions, knowledge of history,
philology, anthropology and architecture are essential for the
archaeologist ashore, a marine excavator still needs additional
training. And what some of that is we are not yet certain.

The most typical case is naval architecture. A diver wanting
to date a wreck would wish to refer to knowledge already
acquired about navigation in ancient times. Yet far from
being able to rely on it, he would only get misleading, tentative theories. For it is on divers like himself that we depend
for the data we need to correct and complete what is largely
guesswork. The fact is that, since we have no important
remains, all that we know about ships in antiquity is the result
of historical research or the deductions of sailors.

What fragments we have are minute and it will not take
long to catalogue them. In August 1864 when they were
building a house at Marseilles, 3 rue de la République, the

6

builders found the remains of a merchantman. One section was as long as 17 yards. A piece was taken away and is now at the Musée Borély. Most of it, however, has been embodied in the building. Some coins of about the time of Julius Caesar made it possible to date the ship.

I only mention in passing the canoe found in the old bed of the Rhine near Strasbourg, the remains of boats found in the lake at Vaccarès, in the Grau du Roi, at Lyons, in the Lillebonne area, and the harbour at Cherchell, all of which were either too minute or too carelessly handled to be of any value.

'There is no instance', Albert Grenier wrote in his *Archéologie Gallo-Romaine*, 'of a Gallo-Roman ship being preserved in a state good enough to give us the slightest clue as to its length or the way it was built.'

Scholars trying to discover the essentials of ancient navigation, including that of the Aegeans, Phoenicians, Greeks, or Romans, have to rely on contemporary illustrations. There are, in fact, plenty of them. Paintings on vases, coins, and bas-reliefs show the shape of ships, even if they do not convey precise dimensions. But mosaics give the most complete picture of all, at any rate of the Roman period. Most important is the mosaic from Althiburus which may be a copy of illustrations to a naval manual of about the end of the Roman Republic or the beginning of the Empire. But part of it is destroyed and some of the ships of which we know the names from texts are missing. The rest are inaccurate and distorted by the artist.

There is another mosaic at Tebessa showing a shipload of amphoras, and there are others in Tunis, especially at Sfax, which go back to the second and third centuries A D. Besides these, some Gallo-Roman bas-reliefs in the Musée Lapidaire at Norbonne and some bas-reliefs at Ostia depict Roman ships.

From all this scholars and historians have a rough idea of Mediterranean shipping in classic times, but nothing short of the discovery of wrecks in good condition can enable us to verify what is often guesswork.

The case of naval history shows that archaeology under water is fraught with greater difficulties than archaeology ashore. It also calls for familiarity with branches of science not required when dealing with land sites. For instance, hydrography, oceanography and perhaps biology.

Some knowledge of winds and currents, experience of life at sea, the technique of navigation, and an acquaintance with sail, are also essential. Without them no archaeologist can really hope to make full use of the chances, open to a modern diver, of reconstructing and dating a wreck. The most welcome discovery, in fact the only one worth while, would not be a piece of bronze or marble, but one that shed new light on life at sea in classic times. To recreate that life archaeology does not need masterpieces of art so much as lots of simple contributory detail. You could say, without being over-paradoxical, that discovery itself is less important than the spirit in which it is undertaken and which sometimes leads to it. The science of underwater archaeology is in its infancy. Of course, experience and research on actual sites will play a great part, but it is on the very benches of the *Ecole des Chartes* or the *Ecole Normale* that a generation of diver-archaeologists must be trained on tried scientific lines. Only then shall we be able to hope for really solid gains from this kind of research, gains which will certainly modify our conception of life in ancient times. Let me try to explain why.

The Mediterranean, fortunately, is the sea most favourable to divers and most fruitful to historians. In its clear, limpid water, scarcely disturbed by its gentle tides, we can see, where the seaweed is thin and scattered, right through to the sandy ocean-bed. There the oldest civilisations have left evidence of their might and weakness. The Mediterranean seems less of a division between different peoples than a stretch of water round which men gather and on which they sometimes fight. Civilisations, gathered along its fringe, have called to one another, made contact, and even when they clashed, exchanged their secrets. This lake, known for so long to man, has seen the earliest tools, the earliest graven tablets, the earliest metal ingots and the earliest statues. All round the coast an almost unbroken chain of ruins and famous names still marks the points from which, since pre-history, the sea lanes have run. You can trace them bit by bit as they thrust hesitantly from the shore. They criss-cross the Eastern Mediterranean, draping themselves between Europe and Africa, and vanish into the unknown beyond the Pillars of Hercules. Along those sea lanes, Egypt, Crete, Phoenicia, Athens, Carthage, Rome, Byzantium, Vandals, Arabs and Normans lost their ships. And now we know that the sea preserves their remains.

In the Mediterranean, more perhaps than anywhere else, men, customs, climates, animals, plants and arts are interlinked. Civilisations take shape and merge in one another. Sometimes fragments recovered from the past mean nothing to us; then we chance on some missing piece that brings the whole evolutionary process into focus. Let me quote only one example. We had to wait for Evans's discoveries in Crete in 1901 before the meaning of Schliemann's work at Mycenae in 1875 could be understood. At sea, the tendrils of history are even more closely tangled. Cretan, Greek, Phoenician, or Roman ships, swallowed up by the sea at different periods of history, now may lie side by side. A diver going down to a wreck must bear in mind the names of all races whose ships may once have sailed these seas, must conjure up their Gods, their skill, their aims and wealth, and bring all this to bear upon the ghost ship plunged in mud, overgrown with seaweed, and only a dim outline in the blue half-light of under water.

Personally I think the abundance of ancient remains will surprise everyone. It is only a short time since self-contained diving equipment made diving relatively easy, and yet relics are already coming to light everywhere, especially along the shores of Provence, Corsica and the Balearic Islands. They give some idea of the wealth of ancient wreckage still in the safe-keeping of the sea. But with the scarcity of divers many stretches of coastline remain untouched.

A new task lies ahead of archaeology: the delimiting and dating, from the evidence of wrecks, of the ancient ports and the estimating of their comparative importance. There is now, for the first time within reach, plenty of material for the diver-archaeologist: stone, masonry, anchors and, above all, bits of pottery. In this way, a true science of underwater archaeology may develop, one which may well change our conception of the ancient world. It has been said again and again that sea traffic in classic times was always coastal, that ships were un-sound and barely seaworthy. From this we have perhaps been too quick to conclude that sea communication was difficult and unusual. But, in spite of this, historians continue to em-phasise the quantity and importance of shipping in antiquity.

Possibly sea-travel was dangerous and interrupted by con-stant shipwreck. But it went on just the same. And however small and unseaworthy we imagine, rightly or wrongly, these ancient vessels to have been, there is no doubt about their number. Without large fleets the constant movement of men, food and materials, basic to the whole history of the Mediter-ranean, would have been impossible.

The legends enshrining the dangers of the deep – Scylla and Charybdis, or the Symplegades rocks at the mouth of the Bosphorus, which closed in on passing ships – should not make us underrate the courage of the old sailors. Scholars have observed how these fables were spread by landsmen and poets for whom every sea-voyage was an adventure. It seems more likely that they were made up by Cretan and Phoenician sailors anxious to deter competition and keep, through rumours of terror, their monopoly of sea routes.

How could the sea fail to be a museum of fabulous archaeo-logical value, when, 1500 years before Christ, sailors from the

Mediterranean reached the Baltic, when, about 1250 BC, Jason took the *Argo* to the Black Sea, and, in 600 BC, Pharaoh Necho had a canal dug across the Isthmus of Suez and sent Phoenician sailors round the Cape to circumnavigate Africa. Between 1000 BC and the decay of the Roman Empire, seamen from the Mediterranean crossed the Red Sea to the East Indies, beginning a regular service to Tonkin. The long chain of agencies, set up first by Phoenicians and then by Carthaginians, may have stretched as far as Senegal, to what is now Kayes, the land of gold, and to Benin, land of tin.

Even in remote eras whole populations relied on sea traffic for the wheat that was their sustenance. Neither Athens, nor Corinth, nor Aegina, had land enough to feed their people. They depended completely on imports and there were sufficient ships in the Mediterranean to meet their needs. When the Wars of the Medes broke out Syracuse alone could supply all the corn the Greek armies required.

Methods of navigation and port installations were equal to the task. We have sailing orders dating from the fourth century BC. There are others going back to the second century: for instance the *Stadiasmus*, showing the distances between ports of call, the various anchorages, landmarks, places to take shelter and take in water. It is no coincidence that the lighthouse at Alexandria, one of the wonders of the world, was built in the third century BC, in the very place where one of the most active scientific research stations was founded, and the world's first library collected. At a later date Rome herself, for all her marble and might, would have perished if she had not shipped corn from Sicily, North Africa, Egypt and the Black Sea. She too erected lighthouses all round the Mediterranean. But the scope of Roman sea-trade exceeded that of all earlier civilisations. Through Beirut, terminus of all the caravans in Asia, it funnelled the merchandise of the East, even of the Far East. It broke in on and exploited the silk route and brought to the West the pearls of Asia and the wild beasts of India.

But the Mediterranean did not only carry corn and the spoils of the East. Since prehistoric times it sustained a traffic in pottery at whose importance archaeological sites are only beginning to hint. Attic and Campanian pottery reached horizons of the Ancient World still almost incredible in their remoteness. And Carthage, through her navy, achieved a temporary monopoly of the silver market, of gold, lead and tin.

Besides, in every period *parvenu* barbarian snobbery or shrewd collectors' tastes ensured the migration of artistic masterpieces. High society in Rome bought 'ancient' Greek marbles and bronzes long before Sulla started looting them. The aesthetic tastes of Berber princes brought up in the school of Athens or the Hellenist civilisation of Carthage, hankered greedily for masterpieces. Under Juba II Cherchell became a museum. Its Apollo, worthy of Phidias, its Athene, a copy of the Praxiteles Bacchus, arrived safely; but how many went down like the ship at Mahdia?

These reflections on navigation in ancient times seem to me essential to my theme. We must rely on them to form a framework for the submarine archaeology of the future. It will not develop of its own accord. Just as archaeology on land is rooted in history and geography, so must marine archaeology base itself on historical and geographical fact. A study of harbours, of the part they played for thousands of years, and of the hinterland they served, must go hand in hand with the exploring of ancient wrecks or the search for relics buried in offshore mud. Looked at in this light, marine archaeology impinges on naval, commercial and economic history. We may even achieve a kind of human oceanography! Its methods and its limits have still to be defined, but when elaborated it will throw much light on a period still in comparative shadow.

There is no lack of material for research or of sites to explore. On the land and under the sea archaeology should be developed on parallel lines. M. Jacques Coupry, a former student of the School of Athens, has provided the first example of this on the site of Olbia, near Hyères.

The Mediterranean is an underwater museum still awaiting its visitors. At Tyre, Sidon, Jaffa, Lattachia, Pantellaria on the coasts of French North Africa, the Hadramaut (Soussa), and at Sala Colonia (Rabat), marine archaeology has its most glittering opportunities. The secrets of 4000 years lie in these undredged waters. The most important may be in shallow water, under a layer of mud only a few inches deep. Ancient history may be offering us another face, of unfamiliar beauty, beneath the waves. All we need is a compressed air-flask, method and financial backing. The Past can then, bit by bit, fulfil its origins a second time: through the stonework of some ancient quay found under seaweed, through coins, anchors, shards of amphoras, and now and then, as reward, perhaps a wreck. But first we must learn to fix reliable dates to every fragment, so that we can piece together from the debris the whole story of man's endeavour.

# 10

# Future Development

DIVING is not only a holiday sport. From now on it will be an integral instrument of scientific research. Biologists, hydrographers, physiologists, physicists, engineers and archaeologists, all use it, not only incidentally, but as a means of extending their territories and throwing fresh light on their own methods. In future, most sciences will have an underwater section.

But how far can one see into the future? Perhaps we can make a reasonable attempt. At any rate, let us try to outline successive stages in the sea's development rather than concoct a fantasy-civilisation out of Jules Verne.

The problems that seem most acute in the first, that is to say, our own, period of conquering the deep, are legal. Like all new forms of human activity, the conquest of the sea-bed requires the establishment of valid legislation. This was strikingly the case with aviation. The development of air-travel set problems in private, public, administrative and international law, that had to be defined and solved: problems of insurance and responsibility, of territorial rights, airports and free passage.

Underwater operations create similar problems, of even greater complexity. Man's intervention in the affairs of the deep means that the state must now act as guardian of all kinds of marine wealth: wrecks, mineral deposits, mining, biological resources. Countries, in the field of international relations, will in future have to come to terms about the ownership, control and defence of submerged lands, hitherto undisputed because they were regarded as inaccessible. Maritime law, so far relating only to surface activities, must now extend to what lies underneath. It remains to be seen whether its principles and statutes can be adapted without alteration.

To discuss this we must skim quickly over the suppositions on which maritime law is based.

Every country with a coastline claims the exercise of authority over a maritime zone of varying limits. 'It has been admitted for many hundreds of years', M. Gilbert Gidel wrote in his *Le Droit international public de la Mer*, 'and certainly since the fourteenth century, that the sea areas adjacent to coasts have a special legal condition.'

Roman law provides no suitable precedent. Roman lawyers allowed free use of the sea for the benefit of everyone: this was the *jus gentium*, a doctrine, in truth, of little value. No disputes could arise because all the seas of the civilised world were included as being within the limits of the Roman Empire.

In the Middle Ages this doctrine began to lose ground. To-day there are two separate kinds of law, one applicable to what are called 'territorial waters' and the other to what is known as the 'contiguous zone'.

Territorial waters are, in the strict meaning given to the term at The Hague in 1930, the strip of water between the coast and the high seas. But this coastal strip has by no means the same width all over the world. It is subject to political ambition, even to caprice.

This is not, however, the place to argue the rights of territorial waters, whether their legitimate purpose should be defensive and their width regulated by the range of gunfire – in which case they would be constantly changing. We need only say that a maritime state has full rights over this strip of sea. The contiguous zone, which is beyond territorial waters, is quite another matter: a state has only partial authority, and jurisdiction over this, mainly to do with customs and police work.

These distinctions have been made with only surface activity in mind. They deal with shipping and do not in any way refer to the sea-bed.

There is, however, a clause in French maritime law whose application certain lawyers have attempted to enlarge, hoping through it to establish legal control over the deep. The document in question is a decree dated 29th September – 1st October, 1929, and refers to the admission of foreign warships to territorial waters, and their length of stay. It forbids these ships to undertake, with or without diving gear, any kind of work below the surface without permission. It is quite clear that this clause was added for reasons of national defence and does not lay down real terms of underwater rights. These must, however, be defined and made legal.

For a long time now mine seams under the sea have been worked. The world production of underwater coal was 13,400,000 tons in 1926. These seams are distributed at various places: off the coasts of Cornwall and Cumberland in England, in the Bay of Biscay, off Chile, Canada, and Japan. In addition there are the French iron mines at Diélette and the tin mines in the Singkep sea off the west coast of Sumatra.

Some of these workings stretch far under the sea. The one in south Durham goes out nearly 2 miles from the shore. One in Chile is over a mile. But none of these subterranean corridors seem to have exceeded the territorial limits.

The English lawyer, Gray, who has done much research on the problem, has no doubt that the legitimate working of underwater mines should not be confined to the country in possession of the adjacent coast.

M. Gidel also expresses a decided opinion: 'The rights of the coastal power over the bed of territorial waters are rights solely belonging to the landward and not the seaward areas.'

But is what M. Gidel wrote in 1932 still valid now, when the extraction of oil from the sea-bed threatens to block the coast with machinery and permanent plant obstructive to shipping?

The drilling of petroleum wells in the sea, at great depths, is now common practice. But this also requires plant on the surface and the permanent use of a certain area of sea. Several of these wells are already in operation. The first were drilled off the Californian coast, in the Pacific. But the sea-bed shelves so steeply a short way out that only three wells have been completed. On the other hand, a great many have been put into operation in the Gulf of Mexico. Eleven are being worked on the Louisiana coast. Drilling machinery and derricks, operated from anchored rafts, work day and night whatever the weather and state of the sea. Wells are now being drilled over 10 fathoms down, and it is hoped soon to reach depths of 15 fathoms or more. This is all being done, it appears, within territorial limits. But others have been discovered more than 100 miles off the Mexican coast and have already been prospected.

These undertakings set complicated legal problems. Differences of opinion have particularly arisen between the coastal states and the Federal Government of the United States. The Federal Government maintains that the costs of upkeep and defence entitle it to claim the rents paid to the coastal states by oil companies. The stakes now before the federal court are considerable. Companies not only pay rent for the underwater sites they work, but in addition have to lease large areas of sea in order to protect their actual field of operations. They have also to pay for prospecting rights. These sites are already worth millions of dollars. Rents equal about an eighth of the value of the petroleum extracted and so enormous sums of money are involved. In the Persian Gulf, where underwater drilling is being planned, similar sums are at stake, though no agreements on territorial rights between the British, Americans, and now Persians, have yet been reached.

It is not surprising in view of the petroleum off her own coasts, that the United States has been the first to lay formal claim to undersea rights. President Truman, on 25th September, 1945, stated: 'The Government of the United States regards the natural resources of the subsoil and sea-bed of the continental shelf beneath the high seas but contiguous to the coasts of the United States as appertaining to the United States, subject to its jurisdiction and control.' This proclamation added: 'In cases where the continental shelf extends to the shores of another State, or is shared with an adjacent State, the boundary shall be determined by the United States and the State concerned in accordance with equitable principles.' Thus, having delivered a kind of underwater Monroe doctrine, the United States are trying to open the way to future agreements about continental plateaux.

In this same proclamation President Truman takes trouble to be quite clear: 'The character as high seas of the waters above the continental shelf and the right to their free and unimpeded navigation are in no way thus affected.'

Useful though this qualification is, it is still questionable whether it goes far enough. If, in fact, permanent equipment for the extraction of oil is going to be installed in the high seas, beyond territorial limits, that surely will be a serious encroachment on the freedom of the sea. Moreover, it cannot be covered simply by a unilateral act.

What, then, is the legal position of the high seas? Many definitions have been tried since the Roman doctrine of *jus gentium*. Sometimes the sea has been called *res nullius*, at others *res communis*. Both these terms are equally inadequate. They were coined, in Roman law, for quite different purposes and are misleading out of their context. *Res nullius* applies to something which, though still lacking an owner, is capable of having one. This is not the case with the sea.

The word *communis* is no longer suitable. If we used it in this connection now, we should be meaning that everyone had equal rights to the sea. But the Latin expression meant something quite different: it conveyed that the object in question was of a substance not capable of being legally owned.

Leaving aside these two unsatisfactory concepts, there are only two possibilities in law left. One is that the high seas cannot be the object of any proprietary rights benefiting any country whatsoever. The other is that each country has equal rights to their bounty.

Does the unilateral declaration of the United States take these legal concepts into account? The precaution it has taken to emphasise that any rights claimed over the subsoil do not affect the position on the sea's surface seems to suggest that America wishes to act in accordance with the traditional ideas of maritime law.

The Truman declaration, however, is of historic importance not only as the first document relating to international law to take underwater wealth into consideration, but also because it has set an example. Mexico, Chile, Peru, and the Argentine have already made similar declarations, claiming ownership of continental plateaux reaching from their coasts right into the high seas. Some Americans wish to go even further and claim control over half their adjacent oceans.

Whatever the rights of all this, there is no doubt that the underwater kingdoms are now a matter of international preoccupation, whether for reasons of national defence, the building up of food reserves, or the protection of mineral deposits.

France, with close on 2000 miles of coastline bordering on three different seas, with the superb balcony of North Africa and the shores of West Africa, is one of the countries most directly concerned in underwater law and regulations. Diving technique in France is more advanced and has been practised more fully on the Mediterranean coast than anywhere else. To the French navy is due the dazzling success and pioneer work with which we are now familiar, for it has led research and encouraged experiments. It has, in continuing its great scientific tradition from Dumont-d'Urville to Charcot, been responsible for the creation of the *Groupe d'Etudes et de Re-*

*cherches sous-marines*, which is not only a military weapon but a
real laboratory for physiological experiment and diving techniques.

It is now up to scientific organisations to follow the Navy's
example. It is not enough for a lecturer at the Sorbonne to
teach the theory of diving. It has to be put into practice by
the students. Every faculty, of arts as well as science, should
have diving clubs to explore the great undeveloped resources
of the sea-bed. The Navy would certainly help.

If we are to get the best out of this new continent opening
under our feet we must count, it seems to me, on new
generations. The sea, in all its aspects, must be a career of the
future for young people, whatever their particular branch of
scientific study.

Unfortunately we shall soon have to think about protecting
the sea-bed. Already some people are afraid of the ancient
wrecks off our coasts being over-visited by ignorant, if not
ill-meaning, divers. Let us mention in passing that the law
considers every wreck to have a legal owner. Anything one
may take away, even without felonious intent, is, nonetheless,
stolen. The legal owner of historic wrecks, like Roman
galleys for example, is the state. But the state's rights would
be even clearer if some kind of list or classification of these
wrecks had been made. For maritime law, as far as wrecks and
the regulation of archaeological material are concerned, has
not foreseen the possibility of underwater exploration. Its two
essential clauses were drafted in 1681 and 1735.

At the moment, Naval Reserves are in charge of the polic-
ing and surveillance of the coast and consequently of the sea-
bed. They do their best, but their means are limited and their
personnel small. They have in fact already been entrusted with
the organisation of underwater fishing. But there will soon be
need of a stricter control over diving, if we want an effective
guarantee of the safety of underwater plants and creatures, as
well as of wrecks.

The use for sportsmen of 'any kind of breathing apparatus in deep-sea diving' has wisely been forbidden. Theoretically, then, fish have nothing to fear from self-contained diving gear. The Reserves take care to see that this sensible rule is observed and divers usually respect it. But what will happen when the number of undersea tourists increases?

Similarly, with stationary creatures: how much will gorgonians and coral suffer from the attentions of too numerous admirers? The Reserves can hardly be expected to cope with that. And one remembers that Norbert Casteret, the speleologist, was forced to seal up the entrance of some grottos which he had discovered. In a few months the public destroyed, broke or removed the superb limestone blooms which tapestried the walls; and they were grottos difficult to find.

Perhaps we shall be able to classify as 'underwater parks' places chosen for the beauty of their position or the richness of their fauna. Sport of any kind, or the collecting of specimens, would be forbidden. We could extend to the bottom of the sea the system of national reserves, like that for instance at Vaccarès in France, the American national parks or the big game reserves in Africa. We might be able to refill our sadly deserted Mediterranean coasts with decent-sized fish. Meanwhile underwater sportsmen can be reminded of the names of Theodore Roosevelt and Selous, the first to advocate the setting up of game reserves in America and Africa.

These underwater reserves, chosen and marked out by the *Groupe de Recherches sous-marines* or at the suggestion of diving clubs, could be entrusted to these same clubs for supervision. There would have to be a special policy towards them. We can only sketch it out roughly. But I imagine these underwater zones as being both training centres for divers and research grounds for marine biologists. Observations would be carried out on plants, attempts made to acclimatise and rear different kinds of undersea creature, and by means of centralisation it would be possible for the arts of diving and its dependent sciences to be practised together. Best of all, an ancient wreck should be in the middle of a reserve so that divers could explore it and young archaeologists learn on the spot the essential rules of underwater excavation.

The near future, then, is comparatively easy to imagine: it is largely legal. But let us try to look a little further.

For example, George T. Renner and Harold F. Clark, Professors at Columbia University, envisage the development of the sea in the form of an 'industrial paradise'. They mean by this that certain islands and areas of the continental shelf could be adapted for different purposes. For instance, as factories using the thermal energy of the sea and extracting magnesium, bromine, and perhaps the greater part of the salts dissolved in the sea. Seaweeds would be treated for alginates, molluscs bred, fish preserved. This vision of an Aqua-Metropolis is cleverly aimed at attracting American capital and has, at the same time, nothing technically impracticable about it.

Perhaps, however, some element of illusion has gone into these underwater plans, so ambitious both in America and Europe. Farms under the sea have been mentioned and herds of domestic fish, as though the ocean were already in full use. But I have tried all through this book to distinguish honestly between the results that have already been obtained and what are still only possibilities. The sea's actual resources are so wide that it seems pointless to speculate on what may turn out to be mirages, dramatic as some of them are.

These resources, however, seem, to date, to be of four distinct kinds: the energy in the sea, the extraction of its salts, the cultivation of seaweeds, and the breeding of animals.

Experts have, up till now, tried to make use of three different kinds of sea energy: tidal energy, thermal energy, wave energy. Arsonval was the first to suggest using the sea's thermal energy to produce motive power; he opened the way for Georges Claude, who, in Cuba in September 1930, set up the first real apparatus for exploiting the sea. It only worked for a few days and then was destroyed by a storm, like several of its predecessors. In 1934 Claude again began experiments, this time on board the *Tunisie* off the coast of Brazil. Again storms broke up his gear.

These operations were resumed by the National Centre for Scientific Research in 1942, and entrusted to A. Nizery, a leading civil engineer. Nizery has prepared plans for a factory to be built at Abidjan, where the existence of a 'bottomless hole' enables water, 6 degrees from a depth of 250 fathoms and 26 degrees or 27 degrees on the surface, to be drawn up near the coast.

Scientists have for a long time tried to make use of the different levels of the sea, due to tides. The first serious attempt of this sort was made by Bélidor, a lecturer at the La Fère School of Artillery, in 1737. In 1922 work was begun on the Aber Vrac'h estuary, 20 miles north of Brest. This has since been abandoned in favour of a huge works run by tidal power and operated by French Electricity.

Wave-energy has not so far yielded results as satisfactory as the other two. The Oceanographical Museum of Monaco, under its director, Dr J. Richard, has so far done the most interesting work in this field. An appliance operating a two-way pump was built in 1929 and perfected in 1930, but it eventually corroded. In 1932 a wave-pump, invented by F. Cattaneo, was installed, also at Monaco, and although a storm broke it two months later, a stronger version was rebuilt and lasted for about ten years. It fed sea-water into the tanks of the aquarium.

This quick sketch of the various methods used to harness the sea's different kinds of energy should at least suggest the particular local conditions that each requires: thermal energy needs a tropical sea where there is a steep drop in temperature as the depth of the water increases. It requires the help of deep holes or valleys of some sort. In addition, the equipment, consisting of not much more than a tube several miles long, is so fragile that a site, to be successful, should be on a coast rarely subject to storms. Abidjan has most of these conditions: so has Dakar, with the fosse of Cayor. And there is another good spot south of Libreville, in French Equatorial Africa.

A plant worked by tidal-power has quite different requirements. The most important is the extent of the tide, which of course varies enormously. The Channel coasts are particularly suitable, for there are tides of some 39 feet at Mont-Saint-Michel, 36 feet in the Rance Estuary, 21 feet at Brest, and so on. A rough sea is good, so long as it is not rough enough to break the equipment.

If these techniques for harnessing the sea's energy exact very varied conditions, we in France should consider ourselves lucky. The Channel provides one kind, and Africa the remainder.

It is not exaggerating if we say that the biological exploitation of the sea's resources has made little progress in the last thousand or so years. Fishing has scarcely changed since prehistoric times and its equipment is almost identical. From a food point of view it has remained absurdly neglected; in few countries do fish, molluscs and crustaceans act as more than occasional foods. Slight as its contribution is to economy in general, it is so uneconomically obtained, that the biological value of the oceans of the world is being seriously compromised.

France probably provides the most scandalous example of waste. Because she is well off agriculturally she has scorned all reasonable exploitation of the sea's resources. She has gone on in such a way that conditions in the fishing industry have become paradoxical. When coastal development and the rich variety of fish to be found along these shores made things especially promising, grasping exploitation quickly emptied the off-coast waters. French trawlers, each time they go out, have as a result to make long trips, often as far as Senegal. To reach the Arguin Banks, for instance, they have to sail for nine or ten days. When they have fished for about five days, they have to return with their catch. Thus, in twenty-five days, they only put in five days' fishing. Naturally, the cost price of the fish has gone up out of all proportion. Such methods necessitate throwing back into the sea any fish whose market value is not high enough and which takes up space in the holds. About 50 per cent of the catches are lost in this way.

The task that the sea has now set us is the intellectual solution of its problems. Man has the unexpected opportunity to reforge his links with the past. The inventiveness of his pre-historic ancestor, the neolithic pioneer, the architect of the palafitte, must in the future be brought to bear on our Mediterranean inlets, our Breton rocks. The toilers of the sea must found a tradition so that initial discoveries, techniques, and strains of hybrid plants are handed on from generation to generation, like the first pick-axe, the secrets of the first foundry, the sowing of corn.

Perhaps people will say that the cultivation of the sea is a specialist's, or a scientist's, job. The first neolithic farmer was certainly a specialist in his own way, his contemporaries acorn-pickers and hunters. Perhaps also it needed more courage and enterprise at that time to till and cultivate the soil than will be required to-morrow to try and apply the lessons of the soil and the laboratory to underwater sites. Be that as it may, I imagine it will take an equal amount of persuasion to con-vince the incredulous.

It would be claiming too much to suggest that the conquest of the deep will bring spiritual benefits in its train. It will not make man either better or happier. But we are surrounded by so much steel, rubber and electric wire that we should not sneeze at the chance of making direct contact with a natural element essential to life – the sea. It would be a great victory over the machine if we were able to dispense with the increasingly complicated mechanisation of our day and prove that we could get, at less expense, all that we needed from natural elements, animal and vegetable life. It would be as well to see, before pushing mechanical perfection to its extreme limits, whether nature might not after all do the job for us.

Naturalists' researches on the larvae of marine animals have no less range than those carried out on domestic animals, crops or vines. Genetics has benefited the animals of the earth and the plants of the soil. Whenever it has strayed into the realms of marine life it has been on behalf of angora rabbits, flax or even petunias. It is time marine biology turned its attention to its own problems.

If in the last resort animals and plants are only machines for transforming energy, the creatures and plants of the sea may be even more valuable than those of the land. In any case, they deserve something of the same interest, a share of the same scientific capital.

Is it even certain that the hierarchies according to which we classify techniques in the twentieth century are definitive? The power of man, which consists solely of physical power, even if we add to it atomic energy, will never equal life forces of other kinds.

Proud as we are, we should not be afraid to admit our backwardness in the discovery and development of biological resources. Splitting the atom is nothing to being able to understand the working of the cell, the greater power of the two and perhaps the one implement suitable for man and worthy of him. 'Who would have thought,' Julian Huxley wrote, 'that the chance dispersal of a seed from the sea, off the coast of Canada, would have blocked half the waterways of England in a dozen years.'

Compared with life forces, material forces are pathetic. Metalnikov wrote in his *The Fight Against Death*: 'I am going to quote some figures to show the creative power of a cell of living matter. If we say that each infusorian divides once a day, and in fact it does so more than once, then in 30 days there would be 1,073,741,824. In two months the number of infusorians would be so great that it would be difficult to express in figures. It would be easier to do it in volume. A cubic millimetre contains, shall we say, 1000 small infusorians; thus in 40 days we should get a thousand million cubic millimetres of new-born infusorians or a cubic metre of living matter. In 2 months, this would mean a million cubic metres, and in 4 months the volume of living matter produced by a single small infusorian would easily exceed the volume of the earth. That gives an idea of the creative force of living matter.'

It is also the only great force that does not deteriorate. These cultures and cells, multiplied indefinitely in laboratories, are almost immortal. The heart cells grown by Carrel from an embryo chicken in 1912 have shown no signs of ageing, to judge from their activity after 25 years of artificial cultivation. Doubling their size in 48 hours, these cultures at the end of a year could reach a volume greater than the sun's.

Humanity's industrial phase, with its mineral resources, mechanical methods, and electric power, has not yet lasted 150 years. It is unlikely to be the last one, or necessarily the most valuable. Let us make no mistake about the machine age: the future will pass sentence on it, swiftly and decisively, the day that man acquires sufficient control over natural resources to satisfy his needs. His stature will thereby be immeasurably increased.

The biologist will then take his place at the top of the scientific and social scale, above the physicist, the engineer, the machinist, now so all-powerful. Making things live will seem better than making them work. The expert on embryos will get the better of the mechanical expert.

If living organisms do not seem to our time to be meek enough servants, it is the fault of our time, not of life. Possibly they need a skill different to the ones we possess and more devotion than we seem able to offer. Pasteur, most disciplined of scientists, said, 'It would be admirable, as well as useful, if the heart could play its part in the development of science.'

The 'humanisation' of the sea would be out of the question if it could only be undertaken through the agency of quite impersonal sciences. The great store-house of the deep to which the diver has access, its caves glittering with their coloured shadows, cannot leave him unmoved. If he is to make a success of his relationship with the underwater world, the charting and exploration of which will be one of the greatest tasks ever undertaken, man must, in Pasteur's sense, allow the feelings of his heart to be enlarged.

One of Paul Valéry's great ideas, expressed in his *Regards sur le monde actuel*, was that we were reaching the limits of the finite world. Every resource exploited, every inch of land surveyed, and from the sand of the Sahara to the ice of the North Pole claimed by some country or other, with even the sky shared out amongst aeroplane companies, it seemed that we had drained the map of its secrets and would in future have no alternative but to snatch away by threats or violence what already belonged to someone else. The slightest ill-will or greediness could turn the world inside out. These convulsions would be on a scale of such physical destruction that the earth would be left barren and man hungry.

But this perhaps is where Valéry's idea falls short: for the world is not 'finite' while whole submerged continents, thousands of millions of cubic yards of water remain neglected. And these must be reintegrated into man's natural vision before the human adventure is complete.

Perhaps it is only because man has failed to harness the main source of life, the great sea mass, that his fate seems so harsh. Philosophers and thinkers have meditated on the human condition for hundreds of years, but this condition was incomplete and the philosophies will have to be rethought. Man cannot possibly have reached the zenith of his development nor taken his rightful place in the universe while three-quarters of it lie amputated. Economy, psychology, ethics, will one day all have to be revised and civilisation itself re-conceived with the sea as an integral part.

# Post-Script

*Quae tibi jucundo famularer serva labore*
*Candida permulcens liquidis vestigia lymphis*
*Purpureave tuum consternens veste cubile.*
CATULLUS,
*Epithalamium for Thetis and Peleus*

*I only know one way of finding out how far one can go, and that is by
setting out and getting there.*
HENRI BERGSON

ERHAPS we should be grateful to the past for having
kept this world, under the mirror of the sea, for so long
in reserve. The door of this magic universe has only just
opened and in this book I have tried to describe our first steps
in it. I have had to call into service various kinds of learning
and attempt an ambitious synthesis between sciences not
usually regarded as related: biology and archaeology, history
and oceanography. I have had to sacrifice the specialist's
caution. The subject, however, made my method necessary; but
now that I have finished, I begin to see the dangers that came
in its train. Doubtless, the reader will have noticed them too.

Those who follow me will probably do better. I hope this
book will soon be out of date; that will be proof that this
underwater experiment has the value I attach to it. I have no
illusions about my work being anything but the first chapter
in a humanisation of the sea, which is itself still only a dream.
That is why the text of my book means less than the intention
that underlies it.

Let me, in conclusion, try and define this intention, this
animating spirit. It is the quality of enthusiasm that will guide
man to his new kingdom and new destiny. It will give him,
as a diver, confidence in the sea, a confidence in the material
resources of the continental shelf, even in the chasms and
abysses of the deep; and at the same time it will give him a

belief in the scientific interest, the intellectual richness, the artistic vitality of life under water.

There is scarcely a book on biology being published to-day whose author does not lament the general indifference to the natural sciences. A recent trend, however; for between 1885 and 1910 curiosity about sea life was considerable. The books of Milne Edwards and Lacaze Duthiers, as well as the voyages made by the *Travailleur* and the *Talisman*, attracted public attention. In the *Library for Schools and Families*, significant title, there were Edmond Perrier's *Les Explorations Sous-Marines* and Wyville Thomson's *Canyons of the Deep*. Works by Professor Joubin, Roule, and Thoulet, as well as by Commander Rouch, reached a huge audience, while the whole world followed the Prince of Monaco's cruises with passionate interest.

This spate of interest, however, soon came to an end. In less than 50 years ignorance of, and indifference to, marine life has become almost incredible. Academic development has grown more and more stereotyped, dry and mechanical. It has aimed at being practical and modern, yet consists of an armoury of terms and technicalities, which, whatever their value in present-day conditions, make little impression on the mind and imagination. Teaching schedules find increasingly reduced place for zoology and botany. Do people really think that there would be engineers and accountants if arithmetic were no longer taught?

In view of this, it is amazing that twentieth-century man has not completely lost interest in plants and animals. In fact, his curiosity remains extremely lively and 'Collections of Natural History' are being revived on the pattern of 200 years ago. I know, for example, such a one in Paris, where the visitor may admire a little underwater museum containing various kinds of plant and seaweed, beautiful *Gorgonia* fans, and sea-roses gathered when diving while on holiday. The interest and enthusiasm which these modest collections excite in ordinary

people show that there is greater genuine desire to understand
the mysteries of the deep than scholars and experts imagine.
In time, and as interest becomes more widespread, these
museums will multiply. And in their own no less effective way
they play their part in the progress of natural science.

The further man explores the world of water, the deeper
does he become involved in human problems. That at any
rate has been my experience. The sea has met my demands
with incalculable generosity. Whether it was a question of
searching for the remains of ancient Mediterranean civilisations, turning over in the sea the problems of life, or nursing
those non-cartesian sides to the soul which claim their own
portion of happiness, it has never failed me.

Perhaps there is, in fact, more to be got out of the sea
than food reserves and increased scientific knowledge; an
element of reassurance, giving us back confidence and balance,
a reminder of true values, a biological wisdom. 'I think',
Robert Gruss has written, 'that diving in self-contained
equipment has created a new race: Men of the Sea. They view
it in its totality, they bear its weight and try and learn its
secrets. I have never considered diving as an ordinary dis-
traction, or even as a sport. The moment the sea closes over me
I feel some great thing is happening. I am filled with a kind of
awe, without really knowing why.' Unless it is that the ocean
depths give us the chance of a new humanism. Yet I think
that we have not quite reached that stage; I'm not yet very
happy about the word. Is it really a humanism, this slow im-
pregnation, this gentle and pervasive enlightenment, pre-
rogative of the 'men of the sea'?

Anyway, the name doesn't matter. . . . It is the assurance we
get from our life under water that counts. Just as there is no
part of the diver's body which remains unexercised or un-
soothed in the sea, so there is no part of his mind not brought
into play. What possibilities lie ahead!

Toulon – Paris, 1949–51